I Saw a Rocket Walk a Mile

I Saw a Rocket Walk a Mile

Nonsense Tales, Chants, and Songs from Many Lands

by Carl Withers

Illustrated by John E. Johnson

Holt, Rinehart and Winston · New York · Chicago · San Francisco

Books by Carl Withers

I Saw a Rocket Walk a Mile
A Rocket in My Pocket

Acknowledgments

Grateful acknowledgment is given to the following publishers and individuals for permission to reprint copyrighted material:

The University of Chicago for "An Endless Story," here called "The Rats of Nagasaki," from *Folktales of Japan*, by Keigo Seki (Ed.), translated by Robert J. Adams. Copyright © 1963 by The University of Chicago.

Columbia University Press and Vance Randolph, for the story here called "Drat the Wind," from *The Talking Turtle and Other Ozark Folktales*, by Vance Randolph. Copyright © 1957 by Columbia University Press.

Horizon Press and Alta Jablow, for "Rival Storytellers," here called "The Big Bird and the Big Tree," Reprinted by permission of the publisher, Horizon Press, from *Yes and No: The Intimate Folklore of Africa*, by Alta Jablow. Copyright © 1961.

Oxford University Press and Peter Opie for "In a Dark Wood," from *The Lore and Language of School Children*, by Iona and Peter Opie. Copyright © 1959 by Iona and Peter Opie.

The Stackpole Co., Publishers, for two "Improbable Tales,"

here called "The Hunters and the Antelope" and "Who Was Most Skillful?" from *African Genesis,* by Leo Frobenius and Douglas C. Fox. Copyright 1937 by Leo Frobenius and Douglas C. Fox.

Grateful acknowledgment for previously published materials is also given to The American Folklore Society for "Johnny Cake," from *The Journal of American Folklore,* Vol. 2, 1889, for "The Locusts and the Corn," by Gustave Lanctot, from *do,* Vol. 44, 1931, and for "The Tyrannical King," from *Filipino Popular Tales,* by Dean Fansler, copyright 1921 by the American Folklore Society; to the *Hoosier Folklore Bulletin* for "Johnny McGorry and the Red Stockings," by Charles Edward Brown, from Vol. 2, 1943, and for "Good or Bad?" by Lee Martin, from Vol. 7, 1948; to Dr. Walter R. Barnes and Dr. Ruth Ann Musick, for "The Greedy Old Fat Man," from *West Virginia Folklore,* Vol. 3, 1952.

Special gratitude and appreciation are expressed to friends and others who have given much help: to Professor Sula Benet of Hunter College for contributing one story as remembered from Russian childhood and for suggesting and translating two others from Russian; to Mrs. John Figh of Montgomery, Alabama, for an unpublished version of "Jeremiah"; to Professor Herbert of Memorial University, Newfoundland, for much private instruction in folklore over many years and for sanctioning theoretically the central purpose of illustrating formula lore in the present book with songs, rhymes, chants, et cetera, as well as stories; to Dr. Alta Jablow of Brooklyn College for contributing one published story and several unpublished items from her fieldwork collections, for suggesting a number of stories appearing here from printed sources, and for helping me in many friendly ways to complete the book; to a friend, anonymous by choice, who has collected for me several thousand items of folklore from New York high school boys, including three stories printed here; to Adriana

Saviozzi of New York for providing a beautiful Italian story from a rare book in her possession; and to Professor Archer Taylor of the University of California, whose studies of formula tales (identified by title in the Afterword) first aroused my interest, and directed me to hundreds of interesting sources. I am also grateful to Professor Taylor for translating several difficult German dialect words.

Additional warm thanks are due to the staff of the New York Public Library, ever patient, courteous, knowledgeable, and helpful in making the library's treasures available to the researcher.

CW

Contents

North and South America

Europe

Asia

Africa

I Saw a Rocket Walk a Mile

North and South America

Strange Story

I saw a pigeon making bread
I saw a girl composed of thread
I saw a towel one mile square
I saw a meadow in the air
I saw a rocket walk a mile
I saw a pony make a file
I saw a blacksmith in a box
I saw an orange kill an ox
I saw a butcher made of steel
I saw a penknife dance a reel
I saw a sailor twelve feet high
I saw a ladder in a pie
I saw an apple fly away
I saw a sparrow making hay
I saw a farmer like a dog
I saw a puppy mixing grog
I saw three men who saw these too
And will confirm what I tell you

United States

The Travel of a Fox

A fox digging behind a stump found a bumblebee. The fox put the bumblebee in his bag and traveled.

The first house he came to he went in, and said to the mistress of the house, "Can I leave my bag here while I go to Squintum's?"

"Yes," said the woman.

"Then be careful not to open the bag," said the fox.

But as soon as the fox was out of sight the woman took a little peep into the bag, and out flew the bumblebee, and the rooster caught him and ate him all up.

After a while the fox came back. He took up the bag and he saw that the bumblebee was gone, and he said to the woman, "Where is my bumblebee?"

And the woman said, "I just untied the string and the bumblebee flew out, and the rooster ate him up."

"Very well," said the fox; "I must have the rooster, then."

So he caught the rooster and put him in his bag and traveled.

And the next house he came to he went in, and said to the mistress of the house, "Can I leave my bag here while I go to Squintum's?"

"Yes," said the woman.

"Then be careful not to open the bag," said the fox.

But as soon as the fox was out of sight the woman just took a little peep into the bag, and the rooster flew out, and the pig caught him and ate him all up.

After a while the fox came back. He took up the bag and he saw that his rooster was gone, and he said to the woman, "Where is my rooster?"

And the woman said, "I just untied the string and the rooster flew out, and the pig ate him up."

"Very well," said the fox; "I must have the pig, then."

So he caught the pig and put him into his bag and traveled.

And the next house he came to he went in, and said to the mistress of the house, "Can I leave my bag here while I go to Squintum's?"

"Yes," said the woman.

"Then be careful not to open the bag," said the fox.

But as soon as the fox was out of sight the woman just took a little peep into the bag, and the pig jumped out, and the ox gored him.

After a while the fox came back. He took up the bag and he saw that his pig was gone, and he said to the woman, "Where is my pig?"

And the woman said, "I just untied the string and the pig jumped out, and the ox gored him."

"Very well," said the fox; "I must have the ox, then."

So he caught the ox and put him into his bag and traveled.

And the next house he came to he went in, and said to the mistress of the house, "Can I leave my bag here while I go to Squintum's?"

"Yes," said the woman.

"Then be careful not to open the bag," said the fox.

But as soon as the fox was out of sight the woman just took a little peep into the bag, and the ox jumped out, and the woman's little boy broke off his horns and killed him.

After a while the fox came back. He took up his bag and he saw that the ox was gone, and he said to the woman, "Where is my ox?"

And the woman said, "I just untied the string and the ox jumped out, and my little boy broke off his horns and killed him."

"Very well," said the fox; "I must have your little boy, then."

So he caught the little boy and put him in his bag, and traveled.

And the next house he came to he went in, and said to the mistress of the house, "Can I leave my bag here while I go to Squintum's?"

"Yes," said the woman.

"Then be careful not to open the bag," said the fox.

The woman was making cake, and her children were around her teasing her for it.

"Oh, ma, give me a piece!" said one, and "Oh, ma, give me a piece!" said the others.

And the smell of the cake came to the little boy weeping and crying in the bag, and he heard the children crying for the cake, and he said, "Oh, mammy, give me a piece!"

Then the woman opened the bag and took the little boy out, and she put the house dog in the bag in the little boy's place. And the little boy stopped crying and joined the other children.

After a while the fox came back. He took up his bag, and he saw that it was tied fast, and he put it on his back, and traveled deep into the woods. Then he sat down and untied the bag, and if the little boy had been in the bag things would have gone badly with him.

But the little boy was safe at the woman's house, and when the fox untied the bag the house dog jumped out and caught the fox and killed him.

United States

Drat the Wind!

Once there was a man who wouldn't eat anything but turtles. He tried to teach his dog to catch turtles, but the dog wouldn't pay any attention. So the man threw his stick at the dog, and said to the stick, "Beat the dog!" But the stick said, "I won't do it, unless you grease me with sidemeat."

The man went to a big old hog and he said, "Give me a piece of sidemeat to grease my stick so it will beat the dog, because I am teaching him to catch turtles." But the old hog said, "I won't do it, unless you feed me some acorns."

The man went to a big oak tree and he said, "Throw down some acorns to feed this hog; then she will give me a piece of meat to grease my stick so it will beat the dog, because I am teaching him to catch turtles." But the big oak tree said, "I won't do it, unless you make the sun shine warm on my back."

The man went to the sun and he said, "Shine warm on the tree's back so it will throw down some acorns to feed the hog; then she will give me a piece of meat to grease my stick so it will beat the dog, because I am teaching him to catch turtles." But the sun said, "I won't do it, unless you make the wind blow from the South."

The man went to the wind and he said, "Blow from the South and make the sun shine warm on the tree's back so it will throw down some acorns to feed the hog; then she will give me a piece of meat to grease my stick so it will beat the dog, because I am teaching him to catch turtles." But the wind said, "I won't do it!" So the man began to fuss and scold at the wind, and he said, "Drat you and the sun both! Yes, and the oak tree too, and the hog and the stick and the dog and the turtles. And let's just forget the whole blamed business!" he said.

The man just stood there a-looking up, and he kept right on a-fussing the loudest you ever heard. Pretty soon the wind began to blow from the South, and the sun began to shine warm on the oak tree's back. So then the oak tree threw down some acorns to feed the hog, and the hog gave the man a piece of meat to grease his stick. The stick began to beat the dog, and the dog began to hunt turtles. It wasn't any time at all till that dog got to be the best turtle catcher in the whole country. So from then on the man and his family had all the turtles they could eat.

United States

The Greedy Old Fat Man

Once there was a greedy old fat man who could not get enough to eat. He got up one morning and ate a pot of mush and drank a barrel of milk, and still he was hungry. He went out of his house and he met a little boy.

The little boy says: "Old man, what makes you so fat?"

"I ate a pot of mush and I drank a barrel of milk, and I'll eat you too if I can catch you."

So he caught the little boy and ate him, and he went on till he met a little girl.

The little girl says: "Old man, what makes you so fat?"

"I ate a pot of mush, I drank a barrel of milk, I ate a little boy, and I'll eat you too if I can catch you."

So he caught the little girl and ate her, and he went on till he met a little dog.

The little dog says: "Old man, what makes you so fat?"

"I ate a pot of mush, I drank a barrel of milk, I ate a little boy, I ate a little girl, and I'll eat you too if I can catch you."

So he caught the little dog and ate him, and he went on till he met a little cat.

The little cat says: "Old man, what makes you so fat?"

"I ate a pot of mush, I drank a barrel of milk, I ate a little boy, I ate a little girl, I ate a little dog, and I'll eat you too if I can catch you."

So he caught the little cat and ate him, and he went on till he met a little fox.

The little fox says: "Old man, what makes you so fat?"

"I ate a pot of mush, I drank a barrel of milk, I ate a little boy, I ate a little girl, I ate a little dog, I ate a little cat, and I'll eat you too if I can catch you."

So he caught the little fox and ate him, and he went on till he met a little rabbit.

The little rabbit says: "Old man, what makes you so fat?"

"I ate a pot of mush, I drank a barrel of milk, I ate a little boy, I ate a little girl, I ate a little dog, I ate a little cat, I ate a little fox, and I'll eat you too if I can catch you."

So he caught the little rabbit and ate him, and he went on till he met a little squirrel.

The little squirrel says: "Old man, what makes you so fat?"

"I ate a pot of mush, I drank a barrel of milk, I ate a little boy, I ate a little girl, I ate a little dog, I ate a little cat, I ate a little fox, I ate a little rabbit, and I'll eat you too if I can catch you."

The little squirrel says: "You can't catch me, old man," and he ran up a tree, and the old man after him. The squirrel ran out on a limb, and the old man after him. The squirrel jumped over to another tree, and the old man after him. And he fell *and busted himself wide open.*

Little boy says, "I'm out"; little girl says, "I'm out"; little dog says, "I'm out"; little cat says, "I'm out"; little fox says, "I'm out"; little rabbit says, "I'm out." Little squirrel says: "I'm out too, *'cause I wasn't in.*"

United States

The Johnnycake

Once upon a time there was an old man and an old woman and a little boy. One morning the woman made a Johnnycake and put it in the oven to bake. And she said to the little boy, "You watch the Johnnycake while your father and I go out to work in the garden." So the old man and old woman went out and began to hoe potatoes and left the little boy to tend the oven. But he didn't watch it all the time, and all of a sudden he heard a noise and he looked up, and the oven door popped open, and out of the oven jumped the Johnnycake and went rolling along, end over end, towards the open door of the house. The little boy ran to shut the door, but Johnnycake was too quick for him and rolled through the door, down the steps, and down into the road, long before the little boy could catch him. The little boy ran after him as fast as he could clip it, crying out to his father and mother, who heard the uproar and threw down their hoes and gave chase too. But Johnnycake outran all three a long way and soon was out of sight, while they had to sit down, all out of breath, on a bank to rest.

On went Johnnycake, and by and by he came to two well-diggers, who looked up from their work and called out: "Where ye going, Johnnycake?"

He said: "I've outrun an old man, and an old woman, and a little boy, and I can outrun you too-o-o!"

"Ye can, can ye? We'll see about that!" said they, and they threw down their picks and ran after him, but they couldn't catch up with him, and soon they had to sit down by the roadside to rest.

On ran Johnnycake, and by and by he came to two ditch-diggers, who were digging a ditch. "Where ye going, Johnnycake?" said they.

He said: "I've outrun an old man, and an old woman, and a little boy, and two well-diggers, and I can outrun you too-o-o!"

"Ye can, can ye? We'll see about that!" said they, and they threw down their spades, and ran after him too. But Johnnycake soon outstripped them also, and seeing they could never catch him they gave up the chase and sat down to rest.

On went Johnnycake, and by and by he came to a bear. The bear said: "Where ye going, Johnnycake?"

He said: "I've outrun an old man, and an old woman, and a little boy, and two well-diggers, and two ditch-diggers, and I can outrun you too-o-o!"

"Ye can, can ye?" growled the bear. "We'll see about that!" and trotted as fast as his legs could carry him after Johnnycake, who never stopped to look behind him. Before long the bear was left so far behind that he saw he might as well give up the hunt first as last, so he stretched himself out by the roadside to rest.

On went Johnnycake, and by and by he came to a wolf. The wolf said: "Where ye going, Johnnycake?"

He said: "I've outrun an old man, and an old woman,

and a little boy, and two well-diggers, and two ditch-diggers, and a bear, and I can outrun you too-o-o!"

"Ye can, can ye?" snarled the wolf. "We'll see about that!" and he set into a gallop after Johnnycake, who went on and on so fast that the wolf, too, saw there was no hope of catching him and lay down to rest.

On went Johnnycake, and by and by he came to a fox that lay quietly in a corner of the fence. The fox called out in a sharp voice, but without getting up: "Where ye going, Johnnycake?"

He said: "I've outrun an old man, and an old woman, and a little boy, and two well-diggers, and two ditch-diggers, and a bear, and a wolf, and I can outrun you too-o-o!"

The fox said: "I can't quite hear you, Johnnycake, won't you come a leetle closer?"

Johnnycake stopped his race, for the first time, and went a little closer, and called out in a very loud voice: *"I've outrun an old man, and an old woman, and a little boy, and two well-diggers, and two ditch-diggers, and a bear, and a wolf, and I can outrun you too-o-o!"*

"Can't quite hear you! Won't you come a *leetle* closer?" said the fox in a feeble voice, and he stretched out his neck toward Johnnycake and put one paw behind his ear.

Johnnycake came up close, and leaning towards the fox screamed louder than before: "I'VE OUTRUN AN OLD MAN, AND AN OLD WOMAN, AND A LITTLE BOY, AND TWO WELL-DIGGERS, AND TWO DITCH-DIGGERS, AND A BEAR, AND A WOLF, AND I CAN OUTRUN YOU TOO-O-O!"

"You can, can you?" yelped the fox, and he snapped up Mr. Johnnycake in his sharp teeth in the twinkling of an eye.

United States

Good or Bad?

"Two pilots went up in an airplane. The plane had a good
motor."
"That's good."
"No, that's bad. The motor didn't work."
"Oh, that's bad."
"No, that was good. They had a parachute."
"Oh, that's good."
"No, that was bad. It didn't open."
"That's bad."
"No, that was good. There was a haystack under them."
"That's good."
"No, that was bad. There was a pitchfork in the haystack."
"That's bad."
"No, that was good. They missed the pitchfork."
"That's good."
"No, that was bad. They missed the haystack."

United States

The Walk

One day a man took a walk.

One day a man took a walk with his friend.

One day a man took a walk with his friend and his dog.

One day a man took a walk with his friend and his dog. The dog wore a red jacket.

One day a man took a walk with his friend and his dog. The dog wore a red jacket with polka dots.

One day a man took a walk with his friend and his dog. The dog wore a red jacket with polka dots. The dog was hungry.

One day a man took a walk with his friend and his dog. The dog wore a red jacket with polka dots. The dog was hungry so he bit his master.

One day a man took a walk with his friend and his dog. The dog wore a red jacket with polka dots. The dog was hungry so he bit his master. The master got angry.

One day a man took a walk with his friend and his dog. The dog wore a red jacket with polka dots. The dog was hungry so he bit his master. The master got angry and he bit him back.

United States

Peter Went Fishing on Sunday

Peter went fishing on Sunday, threw his line in and caught a large fish, which, when caught, opened his mouth and sang:

"Take me home, Peter, Peter, Peter! Oh, mah, ding!"
Peter took him home.

"Kill me now, Peter, Peter, Peter! Oh, mah, ding!"
And so Peter killed him.

"Clean me now, Peter, Peter, Peter! Oh, mah, ding!"
And so Peter cleaned him.

"Salt me now, Peter, Peter, Peter! Oh, mah, ding!"
And so Peter salted him.

"Cook me now, Peter, Peter, Peter! Oh, mah, ding!"
And so Peter cooked him.

"Eat me now, Peter, Peter, Peter! Oh, mah, ding!"
And so Peter ate him.

"I got you now, Peter, Peter, Peter! Oh, mah, ding!"
And Peter never was seen any more!

United States

The Dark and Stormy Night

It was a dark and stormy night, and all the sailors were gathered in the cabin. The captain turned to the first mate and said, "Tell us a story." The first mate began: "It was a dark and stormy night, and all the sailors were gathered in the cabin. The captain turned to the first mate and said, 'Tell us a story.' The first mate began: 'It was a dark and stormy night, and....'"

United States

What's a Silly Question?

Once there was a girl who asked her father, "What's a silly question?" and he replied, "Once there was a girl who asked her father, 'What's a silly question?' and he replied, '*Once there was a girl who asked her father....*'"

United States

The Shaggy Dog

There was a little boy who was very lonely, so his father asked him if he would like to have a dog. The little boy said that he wanted the shaggiest dog in the world. Soon his father bought him a very shaggy dog. The little boy wanted to know if his dog was the shaggiest dog in the world, so he entered him in a shaggy dog show. His dog was the winner, but the little boy was still not sure that his dog was the shaggiest dog in the world, so he entered him in another shaggy dog show. His dog was the winner, but the little boy was still not sure that his dog was the shaggiest dog in the world, so he entered him in another. . . .

United States

Around the Corner

Around the corner
And under a tree,
A sergeant major
Once said to me,
"Who would marry you?
I should like to know,
'Cause every time
I look at your face
I always want to go
Around the corner
And under a tree...

United States

'Twas Midnight

'Twas midnight on the ocean,
Not a streetcar was in sight;
The sun was shining brightly,
For it rained all day that night.
'Twas a summer day in winter
And snow was raining fast,
As a barefoot boy with shoes on
Stood sitting in the grass.

United States

Strange Houses

There was a little green house:
And inside the little green house
There was a little brown house;
And inside the little brown house
There was a little yellow house;
And inside the little yellow house
There was a little white house;
And inside the little white house
There was a little sweet heart.
　　　　　　　—A walnut.

Out in the field
There is a green house:
Inside that green house
There is a white house;
Inside that white house
There is a red house;
And inside that red house
There's a lot of little white babies.
　　　　　　　—A watermelon.

United States

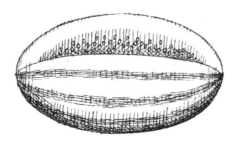

The Old Lady Who Swallowed a Fly

I know an old lady who swallowed a fly.
I don't know why she swallowed the fly.
I guess she'll die.

I know an old lady who swallowed a spider;
It wrickles and ickles and tickles inside 'er.
She swallowed the spider to catch the fly;
I don't know why she swallowed the fly.
I guess she'll die.

I know an old lady who swallowed a bird;
She swallowed a bird, my! how absurd.
She swallowed the bird to catch the spider;
It wrickles and ickles and tickles inside 'er.
She swallowed the spider to catch the fly;
I don't know why she swallowed the fly.
I guess she'll die.

I know an old lady who swallowed a cat;
She swallowed a cat, imagine that!
She swallowed the cat to catch the bird.
She swallowed a bird, my! how absurd.
She swallowed the bird to catch the spider;
It wrickles and ickles and tickles inside 'er.
She swallowed the spider to catch the fly;
I don't know why she swallowed the fly.
I guess she'll die.

I know an old lady who swallowed a dog;
She swallowed a dog—my, what a hog!
She swallowed the dog to catch the cat;
She swallowed a cat, imagine that!
She swallowed the cat to catch the bird;
She swallowed a bird, my! how absurd.
She swallowed the bird to catch the spider;
It wrickles and ickles and tickles inside 'er.
She swallowed the spider to catch the fly;

I don't know why she swallowed the fly.
I guess she'll die.
I know an old lady who swallowed a goat;
She swallowed a goat—it got stuck in her throat.
She swallowed the goat to catch the dog;
She swallowed a dog—my, what a hog!
She swallowed the dog to catch the cat;
She swallowed a cat, imagine that!
She swallowed the cat to catch the bird;
She swallowed a bird, my! how absurd.
She swallowed the bird to catch the spider;
It wrickles and ickles and tickles inside 'er.
She swallowed the spider to catch the fly;
I don't know why she swallowed the fly.
I guess she'll die.

I know an old lady who swallowed a horse.
She died, of course.

United States

The Bear Went Over the Mountain

The bear went over the mountain,
The bear went over the mountain,
The bear went over the mountain,
And what do you think he saw?

A valley in the mountain,
A valley in the mountain,
A valley in the mountain,
And what do you think he saw?

A river in the valley, *(three times)*
And what do you think he saw?

A boat on the river, *(three times)*
And what do you think he saw?

A house on the boat, *(three times)*
And what do you think he saw?

A man in the house, *(three times)*
And what do you think he saw?

Pants on the man, *(three times)*
And what do you think he saw?

Pocket in the pants, *(three times)*
And what do you think he saw?

A nickel in the pocket, *(three times)*
And what do you think he saw?

A buffalo on the nickel, *(three times)*
And what do you think he saw?

Hair on the buffalo, *(three times)*
And what do you think he saw?

A cootie in the hair, *(three times)*
And what do you think he saw?

Glasses on the cootie, *(three times)*
And what do you think he saw?

A crack in the glass, *(three times)*
And what do you think he saw?

Water in the crack, *(three times)*
And what do you think he saw?

Dirt in the water, *(three times)*
And what do you think he saw? *MUD!*

United States

Jeremiah

Jeremiah
Jumped in the fire.
Fire was so hot
He jumped in the pot.
Pot was so little
He jumped in the kettle.
Kettle was so black
He jumped in the crack.
Crack was so high
He jumped in the sky.
Sky was so blue
He jumped in a canoe.
Canoe was so deep
He jumped in the creek.
Creek was so shallow
He jumped in the tallow.
Tallow was so soft
He jumped in the loft.
Loft was so rotten
He jumped in the cotton.
Cotton was so white
He jumped all night.

United States

Johnny McGorry and the Red Stocking

"Shall I tell you the story of Johnny McGorry and the red stocking?"

"Yes."

"Not *Yes,* but shall I tell you the story of Johnny McGorry and the red stocking?"

"Yes please."

"Not *Yes please,* but shall I tell you the story of Johnny McGorry and the red stocking?"

"Yes please do."

"Not *Yes please do,* but shall I tell you the story of Johnny McGorry and the red stocking?"

United States

· 45 ·

Tiny Teasing Tales

"Shall I tell you the story of the two holes in the ground?"
"Yes."
"Well, well."

"Did you ever hear the story of the red hot poker?"
"No."
"You can't grasp it."

"Did you ever hear the story of the new roof?"
"No."
"It's over your head."

"What makes a cat walk softly?"
"I don't know."
"Oh, rats!"

"Do you know why a squirrel runs up a tree?"
"No."
"Oh, nuts!"

United States

Teasing Questions

Where does your lap go when you stand up?
Where does a pig's squeal go when he dies?
Which goes through a plank first, the bullet or the hole?
Which came first, the chicken or the egg?

United States

A Million Stories

"I'm going to tell you a million stories. Here is the first one: There were three men on a boat—Harry, Larry, and Shut-up. Harry and Larry jumped off. Who was left?"

"Shut-up."

"Now I'm not going to tell you a million stories, because you told me to shut up."

United States

The Locusts and the Oats

One year there was a fine harvest, and a farmer filled his granary with oats. He had a big granary, but there was a little hole in one board on the roof. That year there came great clouds of locusts, that ate everything they found, and at last they found that granary full of oats. The hole in the board on the roof was so small that only one locust at a time could go through it.

A locust went in and carried out a grain of oats. Then another locust went in and carried out a grain of oats. Then another locust went in and carried out a grain of oats. Then another . . . and so forth.

(If a listener gets tired and protests, begin all over again: *One year there was a fine harvest, and a farmer . . .* and so forth.)

Canada

Story of a Nickel and a Dime

I had a nickel and a dime.
With my nickel and my dime I bought a hen,
And that hen laid me three eggs.
I have the hen and I have the three eggs,
And I still have my nickel and my dime.

I had a nickel and a dime.
With my nickel and my dime I bought a cow,
And that cow had a little calf.
I have the cow and I have the little calf,
I have the hen and I have the three eggs,
And I still have my nickel and my dime.

I had a nickel and a dime.
With my nickel and my dime I bought a goat,
And that goat had a little kid.
I have the goat and I have the little kid,
I have the cow and I have the little calf,
I have the hen and I have the three eggs,
And I still have my nickel and my dime.

I had a nickel and a dime.
With my nickel and my dime I bought a donkey,
And that donkey had a little colt.
I have the donkey and I have the little colt,
I have the goat and I have the little kid,
I have the cow and I have the little calf,
I have the hen and I have the three eggs,
And I still have my nickel and my dime.

I had a nickel and a dime.
With my nickel and my dime I bought a guitar.
And when I strummed it, it played so prettily,
The donkey danced, the colt danced,
The goat danced, the kid danced,
The cow danced, the calf danced,
The hen danced, the eggs danced,
And I danced with my nickel and my dime.

Puerto Rico

Thousands and Thousands of Ducks

Once there was a duck dealer who owned thousands and thousands of ducks, and one day he heard that there was going to be a great fiesta in the town where he could sell all his ducks. Since he was broke and needed money, he gathered together his thousands and thousands of ducks and started to town to see if he could sell his thousands and thousands of ducks.

On the way he came to a wide, wide river which he had to cross by a bridge to narrow that the ducks could cross over it only by walking in single file. So the man lined up his thousands and thousands of ducks in single file, and since there were thousands and thousands of ducks the line was many, many, many miles long. Then he made one duck cross over the narrow bridge. Then another duck went across. Then another duck went across. Then another duck went across. Then another duck went across. . . .

(The speaker finally pauses. If a listener asks, "What happened?" he replies, "The ducks are still passing over.")

Puerto Rico

The Heron's Ball

The Heron was giving a ball for all the birds, and the Rooster set out to go. On the way he found a ripe tomato and stopped to eat it and got his bill dirty. He walked on till he came to some Grass.

"Grass," he said, "please clean my bill for I am going to the Heron's ball."

"I won't," said the Grass.

The Rooster walked on until he met a Cow.

"Cow," he said, "please eat the Grass, who won't clean my bill when I am going to the Heron's ball."

"I won't," said the Cow.

The Rooster walked on until he saw a Stick.

"Stick," he said, "please beat the Cow, who won't eat the Grass, who won't clean my bill when I am going to the Heron's ball."

"I won't," said the Stick.

The Rooster walked on until he came to a River.

"River," he said, "please rot the Stick, who won't beat the Cow, who won't eat the Grass, who won't clean my bill when I am going to the Heron's ball."

"I won't," said the River.

The Rooster walked on until he met the Sun.

"Sun," he said, "please dry up the River, who won't rot the Stick, who won't beat the Cow, who won't eat the Grass, who won't clean my bill when I am going to the Heron's ball."

"Certainly!" said the Sun.

So the Sun began to dry up the River, and the River began to rot the Stick, and the Stick began to beat the Cow, and the Cow began to eat the Grass, and the Grass said, "Stop eating me! I will clean the Rooster's bill."

When his bill was nicely cleaned, the Rooster went on to the Heron's ball, where he danced all night.

Cuba

The Elephants

One elephant gets in the way of lots of people,
Two elephants get in the way of a lot more;
Three elephants get in the way of lots of people,
Four elephants get in the way of a lot more;
Five elephants get in the way of lots of people,
Six elephants get in the way of a lot more;
Seven elephants get in the way of lots of people,
Eight elephants get in the way of a lot more;
Nine elephants get in the way of lots of people,
Ten elephants get in the way of a lot more;
Eleven . . . . (until the victim can't stand any more).

Brazil

The Pretty Bird

Once in a certain street there lived a man who had a pretty singing bird, and the bird was so pretty and the bird sang so well that there was never another bird like that bird. One day a man drove by in his carriage; he saw the bird and heard the bird sing and he said:

"How pretty that bird is and how well that bird sings!"

He asked to see the bird's owner because he wanted to buy the bird. But the owner of the bird wouldn't sell the bird because the bird was so pretty and the bird sang so well. The man drove away sadly, thinking about the bird. The next day another man drove by in his carriage; he saw the bird and heard the bird sing and he said:

"How pretty that bird is and how well that bird sings!"

He asked to see the bird's owner because he wanted to buy the bird. But the owner of the bird wouldn't sell the bird because . . . .

Chile

Europe

Teeny-Tiny

Once upon a time there was a teeny-tiny woman lived in a teeny-tiny house in a teeny-tiny village. Now, one day this teeny-tiny woman put on her teeny-tiny bonnet and went out of her teeny-tiny house to take a teeny-tiny walk. And when this teeny-tiny woman had gone a teeny-tiny way she came to a teeny-tiny gate. So the teeny-tiny woman opened the teeny-tiny gate and went into a teeny-tiny churchyard. And when this teeny-tiny woman had got into the teeny-tiny churchyard, she saw a teeny-tiny bone on a teeny-tiny grave, and the teeny-tiny woman said to her teeny-tiny self, "This teeny-tiny bone will make me some teeny-tiny soup for my teeny-tiny supper." So the teeny-tiny woman put the teeny-tiny bone into her teeny-tiny pocket and went home to her teeny-tiny house.

Now when the teeny-tiny woman got home to her teeny-tiny house she was a teeny-tiny bit tired. So she went up her teeny-tiny stairs to her teeny-tiny bed and put the teeny-tiny bone into a teeny-tiny cupboard. And when this teeny-tiny woman had been to sleep a teeny-tiny time, she was awakened by a teeny-tiny voice from the teeny-tiny cupboard, which said:

"Give me my bone!"

And this teeny-tiny woman was a teeny-tiny frightened, so she hid her teeny-tiny head under the teeny-tiny clothes and went to sleep again. And when she had been to sleep again a teeny-tiny time, the teeny-tiny voice again cried out from the teeny-tiny cupboard a teeny-tiny louder:

"Give me my bone!"

This made the teeny-tiny woman a teeny-tiny more frightened, so she hid her teeny-tiny head a teeny-tiny further under the teeny-tiny clothes. And when the teeny-tiny woman had been to sleep again a teeny-tiny time,

the teeny-tiny voice from the teeny-tiny cupboard said again a teeny-tiny louder:

"GIVE ME MY BONE!"

And this teeny-tiny woman was a teeny-tiny bit more frightened, but she put her teeny-tiny head out of the teeny-tiny clothes, and said in her loudest teeny-tiny voice:

"TAKE IT!"

England

Titty Mouse and Tatty Mouse

Titty Mouse and Tatty Mouse both lived in a house;
Titty Mouse went a-leasing and Tatty Mouse went
a-leasing;
So they both went a-leasing.
Titty Mouse leased an ear of corn and Tatty Mouse leased
an ear of corn;
So they both leased an ear of corn.
Titty Mouse made a pudding and Tatty Mouse made a
pudding;
So they both made a pudding.
And Tatty Mouse put her pudding into the pot to boil,
But when Titty went to put hers in, the pot tumbled over
and scalded her to death.

Then Tatty sat down and wept. Then a three-legged stool said, "Tatty, why do you weep?" "Titty's dead," said Tatty, "and so I weep." "Then," said the stool, "I'll hop!" So the stool hopped.

Then a broom in the corner of the room said, "Stool, why do you hop?" "Oh!" said the stool, "Titty's dead, and Tatty weeps, and so I hop." "Then," said the broom, "I'll sweep." So the broom began to sweep.

Then said the door, "Broom, why do you sweep?" "Oh!" said the broom, "Titty's dead, and Tatty weeps, and the stool hops, and so I sweep." "Then," said the door, "I'll jar." So the door jarred.

Then said the window, "Door, why do you jar?" "Oh!" said the door, "Titty's dead, and Tatty weeps, and the stool hops, and the broom sweeps, and so I jar." "Then," said the window, "I'll creak." So the window creaked.

Now there was an old bench outside the house, and when the window creaked the bench said, "Window, why do you creak?" "Oh!" said the window, "Titty's dead, and Tatty weeps, and the stool hops, and the broom sweeps, the door jars, and so I creak." "Then," said the old bench, "I'll run round the house." Then the old bench ran round the house.

Now there was a fine large walnut tree growing by the cottage, and the tree said to the bench, "Bench, why do you run round the house?" "Oh!" said the bench, "Titty's dead, and Tatty weeps, and the stool hops, and the broom sweeps, and the window creaks, and so I run round the house." "Then," said the walnut tree, "I'll shed my leaves." So the walnut tree shed all its beautiful green leaves.

Now there was a little bird perched on one of the boughs of the tree, and when all the leaves fell it said, "Walnut tree, why do you shed your leaves?" "Oh!" said the tree, "Titty's dead, and Tatty weeps, and the stool hops, and the broom sweeps, the door jars, and the window creaks, the old bench runs round the house, and so I shed my leaves." "Then," said the little bird, "I'll moult all my feathers." So he moulted all his pretty feathers.

Now there was a little girl walking below, carrying a jug of milk for her brothers' and sisters' supper, and when she saw the poor little bird moult all its feathers she said, "Little bird, why do you moult all your feathers?" "Oh!" said the little bird, "Titty's dead, and Tatty weeps, the stool hops, and the broom sweeps, the door jars, and the window creaks, the old bench runs round the house, the walnut tree sheds its leaves, and so I moult all my feathers." "Then," said the little girl, "I'll spill the milk." So she dropped the pitcher and spilled the milk.

Now there was an old man just by on the top of a ladder, thatching a rick, and when he saw the little girl spill the milk he said, "Little girl, what do you mean by spilling the milk? Your little brothers and sisters must go without their supper." Then said the little girl, "Titty's dead, and Tatty weeps, the stool hops, and the broom sweeps, the door jars, and the window creaks, the old bench runs round the house, the walnut tree sheds all its leaves, the little bird moults all its feathers, and so I spill the milk."

"Oh!" said the old man, "then I'll tumble off the ladder and break my neck." So he tumbled off the ladder and broke his neck, and when the old man broke his neck the great walnut tree fell down with a great crash and upset the old bench and the house, and the house falling knocked the window out, and the window knocked the door down, and the door upset the broom, and the broom upset the stool, and poor little Tatty Mouse was buried beneath the ruins.

England

In a Dark Wood

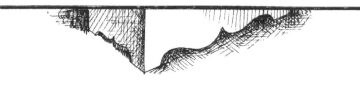

In a dark, dark wood, there was a dark, dark house,
And in that dark, dark house, there was a dark, dark room,
And in that dark, dark room, there was a dark, dark cup-
   board,
And in that dark, dark cupboard, there was a dark, dark
   shelf,
And in that dark, dark shelf, there was a dark, dark box,
And in that dark, dark box, there was a GHOST!

England

Meet-on-the-Road

"Now, pray, where are you going, child?" said Meet-on-the-Road.

"To school, sir, to school, sir," said Child-as-It-Stood.

"What have you in your basket, child?" said Meet-on-the-Road.

"My dinner, sir, my dinner, sir," said Child-as-It-Stood.

"What have you for your dinner, child?" said Meet-on-the-Road.

"Some pudding, sir, some pudding, sir," said Child-as-It-Stood.

"Oh, then I pray, give me a share," said Meet-on-the-Road.

"I've little enough for myself, sir," said Child-as-It-Stood.

"What have you got that cloak on for?" said Meet-on-the-Road.

"To keep the wind and cold from me," said Child-as-It-Stood.

"I wish the wind would blow through you," said Meet-on-the-Road.

"Oh, what a wish! Oh, what a wish!" said Child-as-It-Stood.

"Pray what are those bells ringing for?" said Meet-on-the-Road.

"To ring bad spirits home again," said Child-as-It-Stood.

"Oh, then, I must be going, child!" said Meet-on-the-Road.

"So fare you well, so fare you well," said Child-as-It-Stood.

England

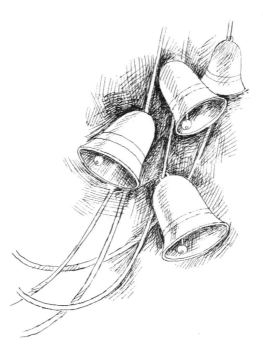

The Key of the Kingdom

This is the key of the kingdom.
In that kingdom there is a city;
In that city there is a town;
In that town there is a street;
In that street there is a lane;
In that lane there is a yard;
In that yard there is a house;
In that house there is a room;
In that room there is a bed;
On that bed there is a basket;
In the basket there are some flowers.

Flowers in the basket,
Basket on the bed,
Bed in the room,
Room in the house,
House in the yard,
Yard in the lane,
Lane in the street,
Street in the town,
Town in the city,
City in the kingdom.
This is the key of the kingdom.

England

The Big Cabbage and the Big Kettle

Everyone knows the tale told by a traveler to distant lands who said he had seen a cabbage so large that a whole regiment of soldiers were sheltered under its leaves from a shower of rain. A listener who was no traveler (yet a wiser man) said *he* had passed by a place where four hundred men were making a large cauldron; two hundred worked inside and two hundred outside, beating the nails in. The traveler asked, "What use would there be for such a large cauldron?" "Sir," the listener replied, "it was to boil your cabbage."

England

The Tail

There was a shepherd once who went out to the hill to look after his sheep. It was misty and cold, and he had much trouble to find them. At last he had them all but one; and after much searching he found that one too, in a peat hag (bog), half drowned. So he took off his plaid, and bent down and took hold of the sheep's tail, and he pulled! The sheep was heavy with water, and he could not lift her, so he took off his coat and he *pulled!* But it was too much for him, so he spit on his hands, and took a good hold on the tail, and he PULLED! and the tail broke! and if it had not been for that, this tale would have been a great deal longer.

Scotland

The Cat's Tail

Once a fine cat went to a barber shop to have his whiskers trimmed. The barber said, "If your tail were shorter, you'd be much more handsome that you are now."

"Then cut a little of it off," said the cat.

The barber cut off the cat's tail and the cat went away happily. But halfway home he stopped short and said to himself, "That barber kept my tail! I'll go back and ask him for it."

The cat returned to the barber and said, "Give me my tail. If you don't I'll take one of your razors."

The barber would not give him back the tail, so he took a razor and went away with it. Soon he came to a woman selling fish. She had no knife.

"Take this razor," said the cat. "Then you can cut up your fish."

Then he went on, but soon he was sorry that he had given away the razor. He went back to the woman and said, "Give me back my razor, or I'll take one of your herrings."

The woman would not give back the razor, so he took a herring and went on his way. Soon he came to a miller, who was eating dry bread.

The cat said to him, "Take this fish and eat it with your bread."

The miller took the fish, and the cat went on. But soon he was sorry that he had given away the fish. So he went back to the miller and said, "Give me back my herring, or I'll take a sack of flour."

The miller had eaten the herring and could not give it back. So the cat took a sack of flour and went on his way.

Next he came to a school mistress, who had nothing to give her little girls to eat. The cat gave her the sack of flour to make porridge for them, and went on. But he was soon sorry that he had given away the flour and he returned to the teacher.

"Give me back my flour," he said, "or I'll take away one of your little girls."

The teacher could not return the flour because it was already eaten up, so the cat carried off a little girl.

Next he came to a woman washing clothes. The cat said to her, "You are working all alone! Take this girl as your helper."

The cat went on his way, and he was soon sorry that he had given away the little girl. So he went back to the washerwoman and said, "Give me back the little girl!"

The washerwoman angrily refused to give back the girl, so he stole a shirt out of her tub and went on his way.

Next he came to a musician playing a violin, and the man had no shirt.

"Poor fellow! You have no shirt," the cat said to him. "Take this shirt."

While the man was putting the shirt on, the cat stole his violin and ran up a tree with it. He sat down on a limb and began to play the violin and to sing:

> For my tail I got a razor;
> For the razor I got a fish;
> For the fish I got flour;
> For the flour I got a girl;
> For the girl I got a shirt;
> For the shirt I got a violin.
> Fee—foh—fum,
> Now I'll go back to my school.

Portugal

In Paris There is a Street

In Paris there is a street;
In that street there is a house;
In that house there is a stair;
On that stair there is a room;
In that room there is a table;
On that table there is a cloth;
On that cloth there is a cage;
In that cage there is a nest;
In that nest there is an egg;
In that egg there is a little bird.

The bird overturned the egg;
The egg overturned the nest;
The nest overturned the cage;
The cage overturned the cloth;
The cloth overturned the table;
The table overturned the room;
The room overturned the stair;
The stair overturned the house;
The house overturned the street;
The street overturned the city of Paris.

France

The Big, Big Rabbit

One day the small son of a farmer, who had been sent out to herd the goats, came running breathless back to the house.

"Papa, papa, grab your gun quickly! I just saw a rabbit down in the field at least as big as our work ox!"

"Son, as big as our work ox? That's pretty big."

"I tell you, papa, it was at least as big as our brood mare."

"Son, as big as our brood mare? That's pretty big."

"I tell you, papa, it was at least as big as a yearling steer."

"Son, as big as a yearling steer? That's pretty big."

"I tell you, papa, it was at least as big as a goat."

"Son, as big as a goat? That's pretty big."

"I tell you, papa, it was at least as big as a cat."

"Son, as big as a cat? Now I can believe you. Yet I have seen rabbits smaller than that."

"I tell you, papa, it was at least as big as a rat."

"Son, as big as a rat? I believe you. Still I have seen rabbits smaller than that."

"I tell you, papa, it was at least as big as a fly."

"Now, son, I know you are fibbing and that you saw nothing at all!"

France

The Three Hunters

Once upon a time three men went hunting. Two of them were naked and the other had no clothes on. They had three guns: two weren't loaded and the other had nothing in it. They set out before daylight and went far, far, far away. Then they went still farther.

Near a forest they shot three rabbits. They missed two of them and the other got away. The man who had no clothes on put it in his pocket.

"My goodness!" said the men, "how are we going to cook the rabbit that got away?"

The three hunters then went on their way. They went far, far, and still farther.

At last they came to a house that had neither walls, nor roof, nor door, nor windows. The three hunters struck three great blows on the door: *Pam! pam! pam!*

The man who wasn't there answered: "What do you want? What do you want?"

"Would you do us a good turn?" they asked. "Will you lend us your pot, so we can cook the rabbit that got away from us?"

"Good heavens, sirs!" the man replied. "We have only three pots. Two of them are broken and the other has a hole in it."

France

When the Bull Bellows

In a wood there is a pine;
On this pine there is a nest;
In this nest there is an egg;
In this egg there is a bull.
When the bull bellows, all the world moves.

> —Wood, church, belfry, bell clapper, sound of
> bell, and people going to church.

France

Mr. Louse and Mrs. Louse

Mr. Louse and Mrs. Louse lived in a little house, and one day Mrs. Louse had to go shopping. She said, "While I am gone, Mr. Louse, please make the soup for our dinner." In doing so, he leaned too far over the pot, fell in and was knocked senseless. When Mrs. Louse returned, she could not find Mr. Louse anywhere. At last she looked into the pot and there she saw him. She shrieked loudly and started to weep.

A passing dog asked her why she wept and she replied, "How can I help it? My husband is drowned in the soup pot, and so I weep." The dog began to bark loudly.

The cart in the dooryard asked the dog, "Why do you bark?" and the dog replied, "How can I help it? Mr. Louse is drowned in the soup pot, and Mrs. Louse is weeping, and so I bark." The cart started rolling backwards and ran into a tree.

The tree asked the cart, "Why do you roll backwards?" and the cart replied, "How can I help it? Mr. Louse is drowned in the soup pot, and Mrs. Louse is weeping, and the dog is barking, and so I roll backwards." The tree began to grow very small.

A bird asked the tree, "Why do you grow small?" and the tree replied, "How can I help it? Mr. Louse is drowned in the soup pot, and Mrs. Louse is weeping, and the dog is barking, and the cart is rolling backwards, and so I grow small." The bird began to pluck out its feathers.

A boy carrying pots to fetch water asked the bird, "Why do you pluck out your feathers?" and the bird replied, "How can I help it? Mr. Louse is drowned in the soup pot, and Mrs. Louse is weeping, and the dog is barking, and the cart is rolling backwards, and the tree is growing small, and so I pluck out my feathers." The boy began to break his pots.

The boy's father saw this and asked, "Why do you break your pots?" and the boy replied, "How can I help it? Mr. Louse is drowned in the soup pot, and Mrs. Louse is weeping, and the dog is barking, and the cart is rolling backwards, and the tree is growing small, and the bird is plucking out its feathers, and so I break my pots."

The father was so annoyed at hearing all this nonsense that he gave a good drubbing to the boy, who threw a stone at the bird, who began to peck the tree, which gave a big shove to the cart, which ran over the foot of the dog, who, with a crunch, bit Mrs. Louse in two. Just then, Mr. Louse regained his senses and crawled out of the pot. Seeing that Mrs. Louse was dead, he thought, "Well, that's a pity!" and he ate up all the soup.

Belgium

The Day the Sky Fell

Once a little boy decided to go play in a pasture. Suddenly he began to run, and soon he came to a little duck. The little duck said, "Little boy, why are you running?"

"Oh, oh! the sky is going to fall."

"Little boy, who told you so?"

"A little piece of it fell on my little shin."

The little duck started running with him. In a while they came to a little goose, who said, "Why are you running?" The little duck said, "Oh, oh! the sky is going to fall."

"Little duck, who told you so?"

"The little boy told me."

"Little boy, who told *you*?"

"A little piece of it fell on my little shin."

The little goose started running with them. In a while they came to a little dog, who said, "Why are you running?" The little goose said, "Oh, oh! the sky is going to fall."

"Little goose, who told you so?"

"The little duck told me."

"Little duck, who told *you*?"

"The little boy told me."

"Little boy, who told *you*?"

"A little piece of it fell on my little shin."

The little dog started running with them. In a while they came to a little colt, who said, "Why are you running?" The little dog said, "Oh, oh! the sky is going to fall."

"Little dog, who told you so?"

"The little goose told me."

"Little goose, who told *you*?"

"The little duck told me."

"Little duck, who told *you*?"

"The little boy told me."

"Little boy, who told *you*?"

"A little piece of it fell on my little shin."

The little colt started running with them. In a while they came to a little calf, who said, "Why are you running?" The little colt said, "Oh, oh! the sky is going to fall."

"Little colt, who told you so?"

"The little dog told me."

"Little dog, who told *you*?"

"The little goose told me."

"Little goose, who told *you*?"

"The little duck told me."

"Little duck, who told *you*?"

"The little boy told me."

"Little boy, who told *you*?"

"A little piece of it fell on my little shin."

The little calf started running with them. In a while they came to a little beaver, who said, "Why are you all running?" They all cried out, "Oh, oh! the sky is going to fall."

"How do you know?"

"A little piece of it has already fallen on the little boy's little shin!"

The little beaver took them with him under a cherry tree. He shook the tree and cherries fell on all of them. Then he said:

"Look, you foolish animals! The little boy walked under a cherry tree and a stem fell on his little shin. From this he thought the sky was going to fall."

The animals felt so ashamed that they all started running away from each other. They are still running, and if you can catch one you can have it.

Germany

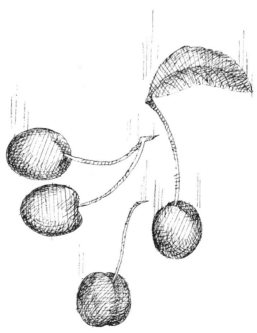

A Meeting of Two Servants

"Where are you going?"

"To Walpe."

"I to Walpe, you to Walpe. So, so, together we'll go."

"Have you got a man? What do you call your man?"

"Cham."

"My man Cham, your man Cham. I to Walpe, you to Walpe. So, so, together we'll go."

"Have you got a child? What do you call your child?"

"Wild."

"My child Wild, your child Wild. My man Cham, your man Cham. I to Walpe, you to Walpe. So, so, together we'll go."

"Have you got a cradle? What do you call your cradle?"

"Hippodadle."

"My cradle Hippodadle, your cradle Hippodadle. My child Wild, your child Wild. My man Cham, your man Cham. I to Walpe, you to Walpe. So, so, together we'll go."

"Have you got a hired man? What do you call your hired man?"

"Do-as-well-as-you-can."

"My hired man Do-as-well-as-you-can, your hired man Do-as-well-as-you-can. My cradle Hippodadle, your cradle Hippodadle. My child Wild, your child Wild. My man Cham, your man Cham. I to Walpe, you to Walpe. So, so, together we'll go."

Germany

The Boy Who Out-fibbed a Princess

Once there was a king who had a daughter who was such a dreadful fibber that her equal could not be found any-where. So the king announced that if anyone could tell her a fib that would make her say, "That's a lie!" he could marry the princess and have half the kingdom. Many came to try their luck, but all failed, because the princess was so good at fibbing that all their little lies did not impress her. At last three brothers decided to try their luck, and the two older ones went first, but they did no better than all who had gone before them. Finally the youngest brother went, and he found the princess in the barnyard.

"Good morning," he said, "and thank you for nothing."

"Good morning," said she, "and the same to you."

"I bet you haven't got such a big barnyard as ours," continued the princess; "for when two shepherds stand, one at each end of it, and blow their ram's horns, they can't hear each other."

"Ours is far bigger," said the youngest brother; "for when a young calf starts to walk from one end, it is a grown cow before it reaches the other end."

"I believe you," said the princess. "But I bet you don't have an ox as big as ours yonder. When two men sit one on each horn, they can't touch each other with a twenty-foot pole."

"Ours is far bigger," said he. "He is so big that when two men sit on his two horns, and each blows a great mountain horn, they can't even hear each other."

"I believe you," said the princess. "But I bet you don't get as much milk as we do. We milk our cows into great pails, and carry them indoors and empty them into great tubs, and then we make great, great cheeses."

"Oh, you do, do you?" said he. "Well, we milk our cows into great tubs, which we have to haul indoors in carts. Then we empty them into great, great vats, and we make cheeses as big as a great house. We used to use a gray mare to trample the cheese down, while it was making, but one day she sank down into the cheese vat so deeply that we couldn't find her. Well, after we had been eating on that cheese for seven years, we found her, alive and kicking and fat. Once after that I was driving this mare to the mill, when her backbone snapped in two. I knew exactly what to do, though. I cut a spruce sapling and made her a new backbone out of that, and it was the only

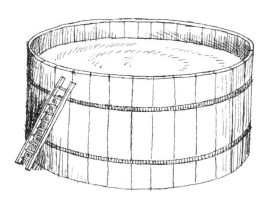

backbone she had for as long as we owned her. But the sapling grew up out of her back into a tall tree, and one day I climbed up it clear to heaven. When I got there I saw the Queen of Heaven sitting and spinning the foam of the sea into pig-bristle ropes. But just then the spruce tree broke, and I had no way to get down. So the Queen of Heaven let me down by one of her ropes, but just before I reached the earth I slipped and fell into a fox's hole. And whom should I see sitting there but my mother and your father? They were cobbling shoes; and just as I stepped in, my mother gave your father such a box on the ear that it made his whiskers curl."

"That's a lie!" cried the princess. "My father never did anything like that in all his born days!"

So the youngest brother got to marry the princess, and got half the kingdom besides.

Norway

The Boy and the Fox

Once upon a time there was a boy, who was on his way to church, and when he came to a clearing in the forest he caught sight of a fox. The fox was lying on top of a big stone so fast asleep that he did not know the boy had seen him.

"If I kill that fox," said the boy, taking a heavy stone in his fist, "and sell the skin, I shall get money for it. With that money I shall buy some rye, and I shall sow that rye in my father's field at home. When the people who are on their way to church pass by my field of rye, they'll say, 'Oh, what splendid rye that boy has got!' Then I shall say to them, 'Stay away from my rye!' But they won't heed me. Then I shall shout to them, 'I say, keep away from my rye!' But still they won't take any notice of me. Then I shall scream with all my might, 'Keep away from my rye!' and then they'll listen to me."

But the boy screamed so loudly that the fox woke up and ran off into the forest, so that the boy did not get even a handful of his hair.

Sweden

The Firefly

I went down a narrow, narrow road, and I lost my cap.
   The firefly found it.
   "Firefly, firefly, give me back my cap!"
   "I won't give you your cap unless you give me some
      bread."

I went to the lady of the house.
   "Lady, give me some bread!"
   "I won't give you bread unless you give me some
      milk."

I went to the cow.
   "Oh, cow, give me some milk!"
   "I won't give you milk unless you give me some hay."

I went to the meadow.
   "Oh, meadow, give me hay!"
   "I won't give you hay unless you give me a scythe."

I went to the blacksmith.
   "Oh, blacksmith, give me a scythe!"
   "I won't give you a scythe unless you give me some
      lard."

I went to the pig.
  "Oh, pig, give me lard!"
  "I won't give you lard unless you give me acorns."

I went to the oak.
  "Oh, oak, give me acorns!"
  "I won't give you acorns unless you bring me the
    wind."

I went to the sea and I brought back the wind.
  Then I picked up my acorns;
  I took the acorns to the pig.
  The pig gave me lard;
  I took the lard to the blacksmith.
  The blacksmith gave me the scythe;
  I took the scythe to the meadow.
  The meadow gave me hay;
  I took the hay to the cow.
  The cow gave me milk;
  I took the milk to the lady.
  The lady gave me bread;
  I took the bread to the firefly,
  And he gave me back my cap.

Italy

A Long One and a Short One

"A long one and a short one! Do you want me to tell you the long one?"

"Yes."

"This (pointing to finger) is the finger and this is the nail. Do you want me to tell you the long one?"

"Yes."

"This is the finger and this is the end of it."

Italy

Asia

The Cock and the Hen

Once there lived a cock and a hen, and one day they went to the woods to get nuts. When they got to the grove of nut trees, the cock climbed up to throw down the nuts and the hen stayed down on the ground to pick them up. The cock threw down a little nut that fell into the little hen's eye and knocked it out. She ran away crying. Some lords rode by and asked:

"Little hen, little hen, why are you crying?"

"Because the little cock knocked out my eye."

"Little cock, little cock, why did you knock out the little hen's eye?"

"Because the nut tree tore my breeches."

"Nut tree, nut tree, why did you tear the cock's breeches?"

"Because the goats were gnawing my bark."

"Goats, goats, why did you gnaw the nut tree's bark?"

"Because the shepherds do not take care of us."

"Shepherds, shepherds, why don't you take care of the goats?"

"Because the farmer's wife does not feed us pancakes."

"Farmer's wife, farmer's wife, why don't you feed the shepherds pancakes?"

"Because my sow spilled my dough."

"Sow, sow, why did you spill the dough?"

"Because the wolf carried off my little pig."

"Wolf, wolf, why did you carry off the sow's little pig?"

"I was hungry and God commanded me to eat."

Russia

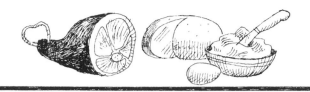

The Visit

"Wife, wife, where did you go?"
"I went away on a visit."
"Did you drink? Did you eat?"
"Yes. I had ham, cheese, butter, and a roasted egg."
"Did you bring food back for me?"
"Yes. I put it on the shelf."
"But it isn't on the shelf."
"Then the little dogs ate it."
"Where are the little dogs?"
"They ran away into the wood."
"Where is the wood?"
"The fire burned it."
"Where is the fire?"
"The water put it out."
["Where is the water?"
"It ran into the mountain."]
"Where is the mountain?"
"The worms gnawed it away."
"Where are the worms?"
"The geese pecked them up."
"Where are the geese?"
"The hunters killed them."
"Where are the hunters?"
"They are dead and gone."
"Where are their souls?"
"In heaven."

Russia

The Turnip

Grandfather planted a turnip, which grew and grew. At last the time came to pick it. Grandpa took hold of it and pulled and pulled, but he couldn't pull it up. Grandpa called grandma. Grandma pulled grandpa, grandpa pulled the turnip. They pulled and they pulled, but they couldn't pull it up. Grandma called their daughter. She pulled grandma, grandma pulled grandpa, grandpa pulled the turnip. They pulled and pulled, but they couldn't pull it up. Then they called the granddaughter. The grand-daughter pulled the daughter, she pulled grandma, grand-ma pulled grandpa, grandpa pulled the turnip. They pulled and they pulled, but they couldn't pull it up. Then they called the dog. The dog pulled the granddaughter, she pulled the daughter, the daughter pulled grandma, grandma pulled grandpa, grandpa pulled the turnip. They pulled and they pulled, but they couldn't pull it up. Then they called the cat. The cat pulled the dog, the dog pulled the granddaughter, she pulled the daughter, the daughter pulled grandma, grandma pulled grandpa, grandpa pulled the turnip. They pulled and they pulled, and they pulled the turnip up.

Grandpa, with the turnip in his hands, fell backwards on grandma, with his feet in the air. Grandma fell backwards, with her feet in the air, on the daughter. The daughter fell backwards, with her feet in the air, on the granddaughter. The granddaughter fell backwards, with her feet in the air, on the dog. The dog fell backwards, with his feet in the air, on the cat. The cat fell backwards, with its feet in the air, on the ground.

Russia

Who Is Strongest?

A hare was running across the ice when *wham!* he fell down. "Oh, ice," he said, "are you strong?" "I am very strong," said the ice. "If you are so strong, why do you melt when the sun shines on you?" The ice asked, "Is the sun strong?"

The hare ran to the sun and asked, "Are you strong?" "I am very strong," said the sun. "If you are so strong, why does the cloud darken you?" The sun spoke: "Is the cloud strong?"

The hare ran to the cloud and asked, "Are you strong?" "I am very strong," said the cloud. "If you are so strong, why do you flee when the wind blows?" The cloud asked, "Is the wind strong?"

The hare ran to the wind and asked, "Are you strong?" "I am very strong," said the wind. "If you are so strong, why can't you blow through the stone wall?" The wind asked, "Is the stone wall strong?"

The hare ran to the stone wall and asked, "Are you strong?" "I am very strong," said the stone wall. "If you are so strong, why can the mouse bore a hole through you and slip through?" The stone wall asked, "Is the mouse strong?"

The hare ran to the mouse and asked, "Are you strong?" "I am strong," said the mouse. "If you are so strong why can the cat hold you fast?" "The mouse asked, "Is the cat strong?"

The hare ran to the cat and asked, "Are you strong?" "I am very strong," said the cat. "If you are so strong, why must you live from the bounty of the housewife?" The cat asked, "Is the housewife strong?"

The hare ran to the housewife and asked, "Little mother, are you strong?" "I am very strong," said the housewife. "If you are so strong, why must you live from the bounty of God?" The housewife asked, "Is God strong?"

The hare asked God, "Are you strong, God?" God did not answer. Again the hare asked, "God, are you strong?" Again there was no answer. For the third time the hare asked, "God, are you strong?" God gave no answer, but let his thunder resound. The thunderbolt killed the hare, and the old housewife made dumplings out of him and ate him. That is the end of the story.

Cheremis People of Siberia

The Little Bird That Found the Pea

Once upon a time a little bird, on its way through the woods, picked up a pea and took it to the miller to be split, but half of it stuck fast in the socket of the mill handle and the miller could not get it out. So the little bird went off to the carpenter and said, "Carpenter, carpenter, come and cut the mill handle. My pea is in the mill handle. What shall I eat? what shall I drink? and what shall I take to foreign countries?"

"Be off," said the carpenter. "Shall I come and cut the mill handle for the sake of a single pea?"

Then the bird went to the king and said, "King, king, chide the carpenter. The carpenter won't cut the mill-handle. My pea is stuck in the mill handle. What shall I eat? what shall I drink? and what shall I take to foreign countries?"

"Be off with you," said the king. "Do you think I am going to chide the carpenter for the sake of a single pea?"

Then the little bird went to the queen and said, "Queen, queen, speak to the king. The king won't chide the carpenter. The carpenter won't cut the mill handle. My pea is in the mill handle. What shall I eat? what shall I drink? and what shall I take to foreign countries?"

But the queen said, "Be off with you. Do you think I am going to talk to the king for the sake of a single pea?"

Then the little bird went to the snake and said, "Snake, snake, bite the queen. The queen won't talk to the king. The king won't chide the carpenter. The carpenter won't cut the mill handle. My pea is in the mill handle. What shall I eat? what shall I drink? and what shall I take to foreign countries?"

But the snake said, "Be off with you. Do you think I am going to bite the queen for the sake of a single pea?"

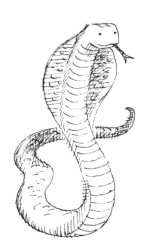

Then the little bird went to the stick and said, "Stick, stick, beat the snake, snake won't bite queen, queen won't speak to king, king won't chide carpenter, carpenter won't cut mill handle. My pea is in the mill handle. What shall I eat? what shall I drink? and what shall I take to foreign countries?"

But the stick said, "Be off with you. Do you think I am going to beat the snake for the sake of a single pea?"

Then the little bird went to the fire and said, "Fire, fire, burn stick, stick won't beat snake, snake won't bite queen, queen won't talk to king, king won't chide carpenter, carpenter won't cut mill handle. My pea is in the mill handle. What shall I eat? what shall I drink? and what shall I take to foreign countries?"

But the fire said, "Be off with you. Do you think I am going to burn the stick for the sake of a single pea?"

Then the little bird went to the sea and said, "Sea, sea, quench fire, fire won't burn stick, stick won't beat snake, snake won't bite queen, queen won't talk to king, king won't chide carpenter, carpenter won't cut mill handle. My pea is in the mill handle. What shall I eat? what shall I drink? and what shall I take to foreign countries?"

But the sea said, "Be off with you. Do you think I am going to quench the fire for the sake of a single pea?"

Then the little bird went to the elephant and said, "Elephant, elephant, drink up the sea, sea won't quench fire, fire won't burn stick, stick won't beat snake, snake won't bite queen, queen won't talk to king, king won't chide carpenter, carpenter won't cut mill handle. My pea is in the mill handle. What shall I eat? what shall I drink? and what shall I take to foreign countries?"

But the elephant said, "Be off with you. It would take a whole host of elephants to drink up the sea. Do you think I am going to assemble all the elephants for the sake of a single pea?"

Then the little bird went to the creeping vine and said, "Vine, vine, snare the elephant, elephant won't drink up the sea, sea won't quench fire, fire won't burn stick, stick won't beat snake, snake won't bite queen, queen won't talk to king, king won't chide carpenter, carpenter won't cut mill handle. My pea is in the mill handle. What shall I eat? what shall I drink? and what shall I take to foreign countries?"

But the vine said, "Be off with you. Do you think I am going to snare the elephant for the sake of a single pea?"

Then the little bird went to the mouse and said, "Mouse, mouse, cut the vine, vine won't snare elephant, elephant won't drink up the sea, sea won't quench fire, fire won't burn stick, stick won't beat snake, snake won't bite queen, queen won't talk to king, king won't chide carpenter, carpenter won't cut mill handle. My pea is in

the mill handle. What shall I eat? what shall I drink? and what shall I take to foreign countries?"

But the mouse said, "Be off with you. Do you think I am going to cut the vine for the sake of a single pea?"

Then the little bird went to the cat and said, "Cat, cat, catch the mouse, mouse won't cut vine, vine won't snare elephant, elephant won't drink up the sea, sea won't quench fire, fire won't burn stick, stick won't beat snake, snake won't bite queen, queen won't speak to king, king won't chide carpenter, carpenter won't cut mill handle. My pea is in the mill handle. What shall I eat? what shall I drink? and what shall I take to foreign countries?"

The cat said, "Certainly! The mouse is my natural prey. Why shouldn't I catch it?"

So the cat went to catch the mouse and the mouse said, "Oh, don't eat me! I will cut the vine." The mouse went to cut the vine and the vine said, "Oh, don't cut me! I will snare the elephant." The vine went to snare the elephant and the elephant said, "Oh, don't snare me! I will drink up the sea." The elephant went to drink up the sea and the sea said, "Oh, don't drink me up! I will quench

the fire." The sea went to quench the fire and the fire said,
"Oh, don't quench me! I will burn the stick." The fire
went to burn the stick and the stick said, "Oh, don't burn
me! I will beat the snake." The stick went to beat the
snake and the snake said, "Oh, don't beat me! I will bite
the queen." The snake went to bite the queen and the
queen said, "Oh, don't bite me! I will speak to the king."
The queen went to speak to the king and the king said,
"Oh, don't speak to me! I will chide the carpenter." The
king went to chide the carpenter and the carpenter said,
"Oh, don't chide me! I will cut the mill handle."

So the carpenter cut the pea out of the mill handle,
and the little bird took the pea and went away rejoicing.

India

The Louse and the Crow

Once a louse and a crow made a pact of friendship and began living together. One day the louse said to the crow, "Go, friend, and bring me some fire." So the crow went and got fire and brought it back to his friend the louse.

Then the louse said, "Now, friend, I shall cook you and eat you."

The crow replied, "How can you talk of eating me? If I were to strike you with my beak, you would disappear!"

But the louse cooked and ate his friend the crow; then he started walking. Soon he came to a loaf of bread that a man had left to bake on a fire. The louse said to the loaf of bread, "I shall eat you, my friend."

The bread replied, "How can you talk of eating me? If you only come near me, the fire will scorch you!" But the louse ate the loaf of bread and passed on.

Soon he met a she-goat, and he said to her, "I shall feast on you, my friend."

The goat replied, "How can you think of eating me? If I step on you, you will disappear in the dust."

The louse said, "I have eaten a crow and a loaf of bread, and I shall eat you too." So he ate the goat and passed on.

Soon he met a cow and said, "I shall eat you, O cow!"

The cow replied, "If I trample you underfoot, you will be ground to nothing."

But the louse said, "I have eaten a crow and a loaf of bread and a goat. What can hinder me from eating you too?" So he ate the cow and passed on.

The louse soon met a buffalo and said to him, "I shall eat you."

The buffalo replied, "I have only to tread on you and you will be nowhere." But the louse ate the buffalo and went on.

He next met five strong soldiers, to whom he said, "I am about to eat you five men."

The soldiers replied, "You would get lost on the head of one of us. How can you speak of eating us five warriors?" But the louse ate the five soldiers and went on.

Next the louse met a great wedding procession in which there were thousands of people. The louse stopped the procession and said, "I shall eat you all."

The men in the procession said, "How can you speak of eating thousands of people, when you would get lost on the head of any one of us?"

The louse said, "I have eaten a crow and a loaf of bread and a goat and a cow and a buffalo and five soldiers, and I shall eat you too." So he ate the whole wedding procession and went on.

Soon he met an elephant, and he said to the elephant, "I shall eat you."

"The elephant replied, "I could blow you away with one puff of breath from my trunk. How can you speak of eating me?"

But the louse said, "I have eaten a crow and a loaf of bread and a goat and a cow and a buffalo and five soldiers and a wedding procession, and I shall eat you too." So he ate the elephant and went on.

Next he came to a great pond of water. Seeing the water, the louse felt thirsty and he said to the pond, "I shall drink up all your water."

The pond replied, "How can you talk of drinking up all my water when one small wave would wash you away."

The louse said, "I have eaten a crow and a loaf of bread and a goat and a cow and a buffalo and five soldiers and a wedding procession and an elephant, and I can drink up all your water too." So he drank up all the water of the pond.

Now it happened that some women came as usual to fill their water pots at the pond, and they were greatly astonished to find that all the water had disappeared from the pond. While they were looking about, wondering what to do, one of them, who had but one eye, spied a small shining object on the bank of the pond.

"See that louse!" said the woman. "He surely is the creature who has drunk up the waters of our pond."

Just then a tall soldier came along to have a drink of water from the pond. The women showed him the louse which had drunk up all the water.

The soldier quickly drew his sharp sword and with one stroke he cut the greedy louse in two. Out came the crow, and the loaf of bread, and the goat, and the cow, and the buffalo, and the five soldiers, and the wedding procession, and the elephant, and all the waters of the pond. All were as they were before the louse had swallowed them. And the women thanked the brave soldier who had befriended them, filled their water-pots as usual, and went to their homes.

India

The Story of Ir, Bir, Dau, and I

Ir said, "Let's go cut bamboos."

Bir said, "Let's go cut bamboos."

Dau said, "Let's go cut bamboos."

I said, "Let's go cut bamboos."

Ir cut one bamboo, Bir cut two bamboos, Dau cut three bamboos, I cut a little bamboo.

Ir said, "Let's make a bow (to shoot pellets)."

Bir said, "Let's make a bow."

Dau said, "Let's make a bow."

I said, "Let's make a bow."

Ir made one bow, Bir made two bows, Dau made three bows, I made a little bow.

Ir said, "Let's shoot a bird."

Bir said, "Let's shoot a bird."

Dau said, "Let's shoot a bird."

I said, "Let's shoot a bird."

Ir shot one bird, Bir shot two birds, Dau shot three birds, I shot a little blackbird.

Ir said, "Let's gather fuel cakes."

Bir said, "Let's gather fuel cakes."

Dau said, "Let's gather fuel cakes."

I said, "Let's gather fuel cakes."

Ir gathered one fuel cake, Bir gathered two fuel cakes, Dau gathered three fuel cakes, I gathered a little fuel cake.

Ir said, "Let's broil the bird."

Bir said, "Let's broil the bird."

Dau said, "Let's broil the bird."

I said, "Let's broil the bird."

Ir broiled one bird, Dir broiled two birds, Dau broiled three birds, I broiled my little bird; it got burnt and only a little bit was left.

Ir said, "Let's go get a stool."

Bir said, "Let's go get a stool."

Dau said, "Let's go get a stool."

I said, "Let's go get a stool."

Ir brought one stool, Bir brought two stools, Dau brought three stools, I just sat down *so*.

Ir said, "Let's eat the bird."

Bir said, "Let's eat the bird."

Dau said, "Let's eat the bird."

I said, "Let's eat the birdie."

Ir ate one bird, Bir ate two birds, Dau ate three birds, I ate the little bird.

Ir said, "Let's go buy a horse."

Bir said, "Let's go buy a horse."

Dau said, "Let's go buy a horse."

I said, "Let's go buy a horse."

Ir bought one horse, Bir bought two horses, Dau bought three horses, I bought a she-donkey.

Ir said, "Let's race my horse."

Bir said, "Let's race my horse."

Dau said, "Let's race my horse."

I said, "Let's race my donkey."

Ir galloped one horse, Bir galloped two horses, Dau galloped three horses, I galloped my donkey.

Ir said, "Let's go water my horse."

Bir said, "Let's go water my horse."

Dau said, "Let's go water my horse."

I said, "Let's go water my donkey."

Ir went to Pond One, Bir went to Pond Two, Dau went to Pond Three, I went to Donkey Pond, and my donkey got entangled in the reeds.

Ir's horse cried, "Neigh-neigh!"

Bir's horses cried, "Neigh-neigh!"

Dau's horses cried, "Neigh-neigh!"

My donkey cried, "Hee-haw, hee-haw!"

Ir said, "Let's go eat mangoes."

Bir said, "Let's go eat mangoes."

Dau said, "Let's go eat mangoes."

I said, "Let's go eat mangoes."

Ir ate one mango, Bir ate two mangoes, Dau ate three mangoes, I ate a small mango—then came the owner of the mango tree!

Ir got one stripe, Bir got two stripes, Dau got three stripes, I came off scot-free.

India

The Ant and the Frog

One day a big black ant went to carry a meal of rice to his uncle. A frog sat down in the road and blocked it. The ant said, "Please make way for me, frog. I want to carry this rice to my uncle."

"You can get by if you creep under me," the frog answered. "Everyone who goes this way has to pass under me."

The ant said, "My uncle's rice is tied up in this large bundle of leaves. How can I possibly creep under you?" But the frog would not give way and the ant would not go under him, and things went on like this till noon.

At last the ant said, "Oh, my uncle will be hungry for his rice and angry with me because he doesn't get it." So he crept under the frog, and the frog sat down flat on top of him, whereupon the ant gave the frog a sharp bite.

The frog, becoming angry, jumped on the ladder of a big old squirrel, and broke it. The squirrel, becoming angry, bit in two the stem of a large gourd. The gourd, becoming angry, fell from its vine plump on the back of a wild boar. The wild boar, becoming angry, rooted up a plantain tree. The plantain tree, becoming angry, fell upon a small bird's nest and broke it. The small bird, becoming angry, flew into the ear of an elephant. The elephant, becoming angry, rooted up a rock. The rock, becoming angry, rolled down and killed the Raja's son.

Then the Raja held a court to try the case. "Who is it that killed my son?" "Oh, the rock rolled down and killed him," they said. So the rock was summoned. "O rock, rock! why did you roll down and slay my son?" The rock answered, "Oh, Lord Raja, how could I help rolling down? The elephant uprooted me from my place. Since I have no hands or legs, how could I withstand him?"

Then the Raja said, "Oh, then that elephant was the cause of all this trouble," and he summoned the elephant. "O elephant, elephant, why did you root up the rock?" The elephant answered, "How could I help uprooting it, Lord Raja? The bird flew into my ear and I lost all control of myself, and so I uprooted the rock."

Then the Raja said, "Oh, then that bird was the cause of it all," and he summoned the bird. "O bird, bird, why did you fly into the elephant's ear?" The bird replied, "Oh, Lord Raja, how could I help it? The plantain tree fell on my nest and smashed it, and I was so disturbed in mind that I flew into the elephant's ear."

Then the Raja said, "Oh, then that plantain tree was the cause of the trouble," and he called the plantain. "O plantain, plantain, why did you tumble on the bird's nest and smash it?" The plantain answered, "Oh, how could I help it, Lord Raja? The wild boar tore me up out of the ground and broke my root. How was I to go on standing in my place?"

"Oh! then that pig was the cause of it all," the Raja said, and summoned the pig. "O pig, pig, why did you tear up the plantain?" The pig answered, "How could I help it? As I was feeding quietly by myself, the gourd fell plump on my back. I was in great pain, and therefore tore up the plantain."

Then the Raja said, "Oh, the gourd caused all the trouble," and summoned the gourd. "O gourd, gourd, why did you tumble on the wild boar's back?" The gourd replied, "How could I help it, Lord Raja? The squirrel cut through my stem. I have nothing but a stem to hold by. So I was obliged to fall on the wild boar's back."

Then the Raja said, "Oh, that squirrel caused all the

mischief," and he summoned the squirrel. "O squirrel, squirrel, why did you cut through the stem of the gourd?" The squirrel answered, "Oh, how could I help it, Lord Raja? The frog jumped on my ladder and broke it. Then I had no road to get out and I had to cut the stem of the gourd."

Then the Raja said, "Oh, then that frog caused all the mischief," and summoned the frog. "O frog, frog, why did you jump on the squirrel's ladder and break it?" The frog answered, "How could I help it? A big black ant bit me sharply, and with the pain of the bite, not knowing what I was doing, I jumped on the squirrel's ladder and broke it."

Again the Raja said, "Oh, it was the ant that caused all the trouble," and he summoned the ant. "O ant, ant, why did you bite the frog?" The ant said, "How could I help biting him? I was carrying my uncle's rice along the road, and the frog sat down and blocked the way. I said, 'Make room for me to pass.' 'Creep under me,' said he. I crept under him, and he sat down tight on top of me. That is why I bit him."

Then the Raja said, "You are both of you guilty." They tied the ant fast with a hair from a man's head; so now his waist is very small. They beat the frog severely with a stinging nettle: so now he is spotty all over.

Central Assam

The Beggar and the Rice

There was a man who was too lazy to work, and who lived by begging from the people. One day he was given a large sack of rice. He took it home and put it in a large pot, which he set at the foot of his bed. Then he lay down on the bed and began to plan:

"When there comes a famine and the price is high, I shall sell my rice, and with the money I shall buy a pair of cows. They will have calves, which I shall sell and buy a pair of buffaloes. When the buffaloes have calves, I'll sell them, and with that money I'll take me a wife and make a great wedding. Then when we have a child large enough to sit alone, I'll take care of it, while my wife works in our rice field. If she should say, 'I will not work in the field!' I'll kick her." And striking out with his foot he knocked the pot over and broke it. The rice ran down through the slats of the floor and the neighbors's pigs came and ate it, leaving the lazy man nothing but the broken jar.

Laos

The Tale of a Frog

"Heron, heron, why are you so lean?"

"I am lean because the shrimp don't come upstream."

"Shrimp, shrimp, why don't you come upstream?"

"I don't come upstream because the grass grows too thick."

"Grass, grass, why do you grow so thick?"

"I grow so thick because the water buffalo doesn't eat me."

"Buffalo, buffalo, why don't you eat the grass?"

"I don't eat the grass because the stake won't let me go."

"Stake, stake, why don't you let the buffalo go?"

"I don't let the buffalo go because the herdboy neglects his work."

"Herdboy, herdboy, why do you neglect your work?"

"I neglect my work because my stomach is empty."

"Stomach, stomach, why are you empty?"

"I am empty because the rice isn't cooked."

"Rice, rice, why aren't you cooked?"

"I am not cooked because the firewood is wet."

"Firewood, firewood, why are you wet?"

"I am wet because the rain never stops falling."

"Rain, rain, why do you never stop falling?"

"I never stop falling because the frog scratches his back."

"Frog, frog, why do you scratch your back?"

"I scratch my back because my ancestors have always scratched their backs. Why shouldn't I scratch mine?"

Shan People of Southern Annam

Who Is the Mightiest?

The King is mightiest:
He can have the thief captured and executed.

But the thief is also mighty:
He catches and kills the chicken.

Also the chicken is mighty:
It catches and eats the worm.

But the worm too has his might:
He gnaws through the foot of the King and the King falls.

So who is mightiest?

Vietnam

Plop!

Many, many years ago there were six rabbits who lived on the shore of a lake, in a forest. One fine day, a big ripe fruit on one of the biggest trees fell down into the lake, making a loud "plop!" when it hit the water. The rabbits were terrified, not knowing what the noise could be, and at once made off as fast as their four legs could carry them.

A fox saw them fleeing and called out, "Why are you flying?" The rabbits said, "Plop is coming!" When the fox heard this, he immediately started to flee with them. Next they ran into a monkey, who queried, "Why are you in such a hurry?" "Plop is coming!" replied the fox. So the monkey also joined in their flight.

Thus the news spread from mouth to mouth until a deer, a pig, a buffalo, a rhinoceros, an elephant, a black bear, a brown bear, a leopard, a tiger, and a lion were all running away, helter-skelter.

They had no thought at all, except to fly. The faster they ran, the more frightened they became.

At the foot of the hill there lived a lion with a great long mane. When he caught sight of the other lion running, he roared to him, "Brother, you have claws and teeth and you are the strongest of all animals. Why are you running like mad?"

"Plop is coming!" the running lion panted.

"Who's Plop? What is he?" the lion with the long mane demanded.

"Well, I really don't know," he faltered.

"Why make such a fuss then?" the long-maned lion went on. "Let's find out what it is first. Who told you about it?"

"The tiger told me."

The inquisitive lion with the long mane asked the tiger, who said that the leopard had told him, so the lion turned to the leopard, and the leopard answered that he had heard it from the brown bear. The question was passed on to the brown bear, who said he had heard it from the black bear. In this way, the black bear, the elephant, the rhinoceros, the buffalo, the pig and the deer were all asked, one by one, and each of them said he was told by someone else. Finally it came down to the fox's testimony, and he said, "The rabbits told me." Then the lion went up to the rabbits, who squeaked in chorus:

"All six of us heard this terrible Plop with our own ears. Come with us, we'll show you where we heard him."

They led him to the forest, and pointing at it, they said, "The terrible Plop is there."

Just at this moment another big fruit fell from the tree and dropped into the water with a deep "plop!"

The lion sneered. "Now, look, all of you!" he said. "You've all seen what that plop is. It's only the sound of a fruit dropping into the water. What is so terrifying about that? You almost ran your legs off!"

They breathed a sigh of relief. The panic was all for naught.

Tibet

A Prince Went Hunting

Once a young prince went walking with his crossbow in the royal garden behind his father's palace. All at once he heard a locust singing from the boughs of a high tree. The prince drew near the tree and saw the locust, singing happily in the thought that it had found a safe place to rest in the morning breeze.

The locust little knew that it was in danger from a mantis, who, skipping through the boughs of the tree, was just then stretching out its claws to seize and eat the locust.

But while the mantis was thinking only of catching the locust, it little knew that it was itself in danger from a goldfinch, who, fluttering to and fro in the green shade, was now intent upon catching and eating the mantis.

And while the goldfinch was thinking only of catching the mantis, he little knew that the young prince was standing there with his crossbow raised, eager to shoot him.

And while the young prince was thinking only of shooting the goldfinch, he little knew that he was standing on the edge of a ditch.

The young prince slipped suddenly into the ditch, wetting his shoes and clothing. His fall startled the gold-finch, who flew swiftly away. The whir of the goldfinch's wings frightened the mantis, who darted off to his hole, leaving the locust to finish his happy song in peace.

China

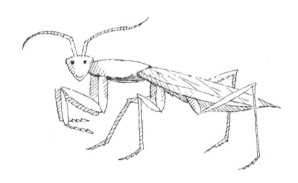

Chinese Rival Storytellers

Some men were bragging about their home villages. One man said that in his village there lived a giant so big that when he stood with his feet on the ground his head reached the sky.

"We have a bigger man than that," boasted a man from another village. "His upper lip touches the sky and his lower lip touches the ground."

"Then where is his body?" asked the first speaker.

"I have only seen him with his mouth open," replied the other.

China

The Rats of Nagasaki

Long ago all the rats in Nagasaki got together and decided that since there was nothing left to eat in Nagasaki, they would cross over to Satsuma. They boarded a ship and set out. It happened that on the way they met a ship on which all the rats in Satsuma had gone aboard, intending to go to Nagasaki. They asked one another how things were and discovered that there was nothing to eat in either Satsuma or Nagasaki. There was no use in going to Nagasaki nor any use in going to Satsuma, so they decided to jump into the sea and drown.

The first rat began to cry, *chu chu,* and jumped over with a splash. Then another rat cried, *chu chu,* and jumped over with a splash. Then another cried, *chu chu,* and jumped over with a splash. . . .

Japan

The Frogs of Yonder Mountain Cry

The frogs of yonder mountain cry. Why do they cry? Is it for cold that they cry? Is it for hunger that they cry?

"If you are hungry, till the rice field."
　"It is dirty work to till the rice field."
"If it is dirty work, then wash."
　"It is too cold to wash."
"If it is cold, warm yourselves by the fire."
　"It is too hot by the fire."
"If it is too hot, move further away."
　"If we move further away, the fleas will bite us."
"If the fleas bite you, kill them."
　"It is too pitiful to kill the poor things."
"If you pity them so much, embrace them and sleep with
　　them."
　"If we sleep with them, they will bite us."
"If the fleas bite you, kill them."
　"It is too pitiful to kill the poor things."
"If you pity them so much, embrace them and sleep with
　　them."
　"If we sleep with them, they will bite us."
"If the fleas bite you, kill them."
　"It is too pitiful . . . ."

The Tyrannical King

Once there lived a king so tyrannical that he made a law forbidding people from talking loudly. Even then he was not satisfied, so he ordered the law to be enforced among the animals too.

One day an officer of the king heard a frog croak. So he caught the frog and carried it before the king to be tried for breaking the law. The king began the trial by saying to the frog, "Don't you know there is a law forbidding people and animals from talking?"

"Yes, Your Majesty," replied the frog, "but I was just laughing, and I could not help it. I could not help laughing at seeing the snail carry his house about with him wherever he goes."

This answer seemed reasonable to the king. So he dismissed the frog and summoned the snail for trial. "Why do you always carry your house about with you?" the king asked the snail.

"I always carry my house with me," replied the snail, "because the firefly always carries fire. I am afraid he will set fire to my house and burn it."

The snail's answer seemed reasonable to the king, so he dismissed him and summoned the firefly for trial.

"Why do you always carry fire with you?" the king asked the firefly.

"I must always carry fire with me to keep the mosquito from biting me," replied the firefly.

The answer seemed reasonable, so the king dismissed the firefly and summoned the mosquito.

"Why are you always trying to bite someone?" the king asked the mosquito.

"Why, Your Majesty," replied the mosquito, "I can not live unless I bite someone."

By now the king was tired of the long trial and he decided to end it. So he said to the mosquito, "From now on I forbid you to bite anybody! You have no right to do so."

The mosquito protested that the sentence was unfair. This made the king angry, and he seized his gavel to crush the mosquito with it. But when the mosquito saw what the king intended to do, he flew up and lighted on the king's forehead. This insult made the king still angrier, so he hit the mosquito very hard with his gavel. He killed the mosquito, but in doing so he also put an end to his own tyranny.

Philippine Islands

Africa

How a Boy Got a Baboon

There was once a boy who set a trap at the root of a tree by a waterfall, and he caught a bird. He ran with the bird to his hut, where his mother told him to go to a distant field and drive crows away from the grain. The boy said, "Mother, roast this bird for me," and the mother said, "Yes."

Well, while the boy was gone his mother killed the bird and plucked and roasted it, and ate it. When the boy came back and asked for the bird, the mother said, "I have eaten it." Then the boy cried:

"Mother, give me my bird!

Mother, give me my bird,

Which I caught at the root of the tree by the waterfall!"

The mother gave him some corn, which he put on top of a tree stump, and the termites came out and ate it. The boy cried to the termites:

"Termites, give me back my corn!

Termites, give me back my corn,

Corn my mother gave me,

Mother ate my bird,

Which I caught at the root of the tree by the waterfall!"

The termites made some earthen pots and gave them
to him. He took them to the brook to fill them with water,
but the brook carried them under the cataract, which
broke them. Then the boy cried:

"Cataract, give me back my pots!
Cataract give me back my pots,
Pots the termites gave me,
Termites ate up my corn,
Corn my mother gave me,
Mother ate my bird,
Which I caught at the root of the tree by the
waterfall!"

The cataract gave him a fish, which a hawk flew down
and took away. The boy cried:

"Hawk, give me back my fish!
Hawk, give me back my fish,
Fish the cataract gave me,
Cataract broke my pots,
Pots the termites gave me,
Termites ate up my corn,
Corn my mother gave me,
Mother ate my bird,
Which I caught at the root of the tree by the
waterfall!"

The hawk dropped a feather for him, but the wind carried it away. The boy cried:

    "Wind, give me back my feather!
    Wind, give me back my feather,
    Feather the hawk gave me,
    Hawk ate up my fish,
    Fish the cataract gave me,
    Cataract broke my pots,
    Pots the termites gave me,
    Termites ate up my corn,
    Corn my mother gave me,
    Mother ate my bird,
    Which I caught at the root of the tree by the waterfall!"

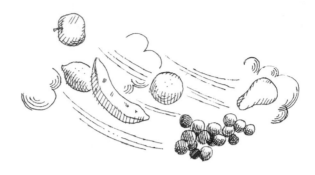

The wind blew fruits down off a tree for him, but the baboon came and picked them and ate them. The boy cried:

> "Baboon, give me back my fruits!
> Baboon, give me back my fruits,
> Fruits the wind blew down for me,
> Wind carried away my feather,
> Feather the hawk gave me,
> Hawk ate up my fish,
> Fish the cataract gave me,
> Cataract broke my pots,
> Pots the termites gave me,
> Termites ate up my corn,
> Corn my mother gave me,
> Mother ate my bird,
> Which I caught at the root of the tree by the waterfall!"

"Well," said the baboon, "I have nothing to give." So the boy tied up the baboon and carried him into the town.

Temne People of Sierra Leone or Liberia

How a Young Man Became a Chief

A young man had some honey. He gave it to his grandmother to keep for him and went away. She ate it. On his return he asked for it. Since she could not give him back the honey she gave him some corn. He took the corn away and piled it on the ground.

Some hens came and found the corn. He said to them, "Say, you hens, aren't you the great eaters!" He let them eat up his corn, and then he asked for it back. They gave him an egg in exchange.

He took the egg and went on. Soon he met some shepherds who were playing ball. He said to them, "You are playing badly! Let me see your ball."

They gave it to him. He gave them back the egg, saying, "Hit with my ball; throw yours away."

They hit the egg and it broke. He said, "Give me my ball. I want to go now."

"It is broken," they said.

"Then pay me for it."

They gave him some shepherds' staffs.

He went on and met some elephants.

"Say!" he said to the elephants, "aren't you the strong fellows!"

"Yes," they replied.

"If you are so strong, break these staffs."

They broke the staffs.

"Pay me for my staffs!" he demanded.

"It was you," they said, "who asked us to try our strength." But they gave him a knife.

He went on and came to some men skinning an ox. They were using slivers of reed.

"Those slivers of reed are no good," he said. "Throw them away; use this knife."

He gave them the knife. They skinned their ox with it and laid the knife down beside the skin.

He hid the knife. Then he said to them, "Give me back my knife!"

They looked for the knife but could not find it.

"Pay me for my knife," he said. They gave him the tail of the ox and he went away.

He came to the edge of a swamp. There he planted the tail in the mud and called out for help. Some people came and found him.

"Pull out my ox!" he said to them. "My ox has sunk in the mud."

They pulled and pulled, but they only pulled out the the tail.

"You have pulled my ox in two," he said to them. "You must pay me for it."

They all paid. There were one hundred people in all. Each gave him an ox. Now he had one hundred oxen and he became a chief.

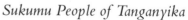

Sukumu People of Tanganyika

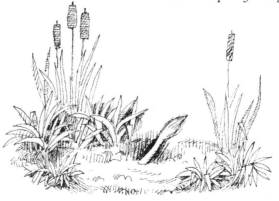

The Big Tree and the Big Bird

Two tellers of tales were engaged in a contest to determine which of them could relate the most outlandish story. The first began: "At the time of the Creation there was just one bird, but what a bird that was! It was of such tremendous size that, even when it flew fastest—and that bird could fly faster than the speed of a bullet—it took seven days and nights just for its neck to pass overhead."

The other storyteller said: "Also at the time of the Creation there was a giant tree. So tall was this tree that no one could see its top branches, for it stretched into the sky. As for its girth, you must know that all the angels cut and chopped at that tree for a year, and still could not cut it down."

"Oh, no," said the first man. "We know that just one angel can move the whole world, so what sort of tree could this be that all the angels chopped and yet could not cut down?"

The second story teller answered, "Well, if God had not created such a tree, where would your bird find a place to sit down?"

Vai People of Liberia

The Hunters and the Antelope

Two youths went hunting and they saw an antelope. The younger drew his bow and shot an arrow at the antelope. At the very instant he shot, the older youth jumped up, ran to the antelope, killed it, skinned it, and cut it up, laid the hide to dry in the sun, and packed the meat in a carrying sack. Just as he finished, the arrow arrived through the air. He caught it with one hand and shouted to his younger companion, "Hey, there! What do you mean by trying to shoot holes in my sack?"

Mandingo People of the Western Sudan

Who Was Most Skillful?

Three young men set out on a journey. One had been turned out by his father because he heard so well. The second had been turned out by his father because he counted so well, and the third had been turned out by his father because he saw so well.

The three young men had a sack of millet. They loaded the grain on a boat. As they were in midstream the one who heard so well said: "A grain of millet has just fallen into the water. I heard it distinctly." The one who saw so well said: "I'll look for it at once," and jumped overboard. The one who counted so well counted all the grain in the sack of millet and said: "He is right. There is one grain missing." In the same second the young man who saw so well reappeared on the surface of the water and said: "Here it is."

Mandingo People of the Western Sudan

Goso the Teacher

There was a teacher who taught children to read under a calabash tree, and this teacher's name was Goso, and one day a gazelle came and climbed up the calabash tree and threw down a calabash, and it struck the teacher, and he died. The scholars took their teacher and went and buried him. When they had finished burying him they said, "Let us go and look for him who threw down the calabash which struck our teacher Goso, and when we get him let us kill him."

Then they said, "What threw down the calabash was the south wind. It blew, and threw down the calabash, and it struck our teacher: and let us go and look for the south wind, and beat it."

And they took the south wind and beat it and the south wind said, "I am the south wind; you are beating me. What have I done?" And they said, "It was you, south wind, who threw down the calabash, and it struck our teacher Goso. You should not do it." And the south wind said, "If I were the chief, should I be stopped by a mud wall?"

And they went and took the mud wall and beat it. And the mud wall said, "Do you beat me? What have I done?" And they said, "You, mud wall, stop the south wind, and the south wind threw down the calabash and it struck our teacher Goso. You should not do it." And the mud wall said, "If I were the chief, should I be bored through by the rat?"

And they went and took the rat and beat it, and the rat said, "Do you beat me? What have I done?" And they said, "You, rat, bore through the mud wall, who stops the south wind, and the south wind threw down the calabash and it struck our teacher Goso. You should not do it." And the rat said, "If I were the chief, should I be eaten by the cat?"

And they went and looked for the cat, and took it and beat it, and the cat said, "Do you beat me? What have I done?" And the children said, "You are the cat that eats the rat, and the rat bores through the mud wall, who stops the south wind, and the south wind threw down a calabash and it struck our teacher Goso. You should not do it." And the cat said, "If I were the chief, should I be tied by a rope?"

And they went and took the rope and beat it, and the rope said, "I am a rope; you are beating me. What have I done?" And they said, "You are the rope which ties the cat, and the cat eats the rat, and the rat bores through the mud wall, who stops the south wind, and the south wind threw down a calabash and it struck our teacher Goso. You should not do it." And the rope said, "If I were the chief, should I be cut by a knife?"

And they went and took the knife and beat it, and the knife said, "Do you beat me? What have I done?" And they said, "You are the knife which cuts the rope, and the rope ties the cat, and the cat eats the rat, and the rat bores through the mud wall, who stops the south wind, and the south wind threw down a calabash and it struck our teacher Goso. You should not do it." And the knife said, "If I were

the chief, should I be consumed by fire?"

And they went and took the fire and beat it, and the fire said, "Do you beat me? What have I done?" And they said, "You are the fire which consumes the knife, and the knife cuts the rope, and the rope ties the cat, and the cat eats the rat, and the rat bores through the mud wall, who stops the south wind, and the south wind threw down a calabash and it struck our teacher Goso. You should not do it." And the fire said, "If I were the chief, should I be put out by water?"

And they went and took the water and beat it, and the water said, "Do you beat me? What have I done?" And they said, "You are the water which puts out fire, and the fire consumes the knife, and the knife cuts the rope, and the rope ties the cat, and the cat eats the rat, and the rat bores through the mud wall, who stops the south wind, and the south wind threw down a calabash and it struck our teacher Goso. You should not do it." And the water said, "If I were the chief, should I be drunk by ox?"

And they went and took the ox and beat it, and the ox said, "Do you beat me? What have I done?" And they said, "You are the ox which drinks the water, and the water puts out fire, and the fire consumes the knife, and the knife cuts the rope, and the rope ties the cat, and the cat eats the rat, and the rat bores through the mud wall, who stops the south wind, and the south wind threw down a calabash and it struck our teacher Goso. You should not do it." And the ox said, "If I, the ox, were the chief, would I be stuck to by a tick?"

And they went and took the tick and beat it and the tick said, "Do you beat me? What have I done?" And they said, "You are the tick which sticks to the ox, and the ox drinks the water, and the water puts out fire, and the fire consumes the knife, and the knife cuts the rope, and the rope ties the cat, and the cat eats the rat, and the rat bores through the mud wall, who stops the south wind, and the south wind threw down a calabash and it struck our teacher Goso. You should not do it." And the tick said, "If I were the chief, should I be eaten by the gazelle?"

And they went and searched for the gazelle, and when they found it they took and beat it, and the gazelle said, "I am the gazelle. Do you beat me? What have I done?" And they said, "You are the gazelle which eats the tick, and the tick sticks to the ox, and the ox drinks the water, and the water puts out the fire, and the fire consumes the knife, and the knife cuts the rope, and the rope ties the cat, and the cat eats the rat, and the rat bores through the mud wall, and the mud wall stops the south wind, and the south wind threw down a calabash, and it struck our teacher Goso. You should not do it."

And the gazelle held its tongue without saying a word. And they said, "This is the one who threw down the calabash, and it struck our teacher Goso, and we will kill him." And they took the gazelle and they killed it.

Zanzibar

Afterword

I SAW A ROCKET WALK A MILE is a book designed primarily for the pleasure of young readers, and to grownups it should prove an entertaining, and even instructive, excursion along one fascinating highway of world folklore. Along the way they will find many pleasing items to read or tell to young listeners. The seventy or more folktales, chants, and songs which are gathered here from many lands are of kinds that have delighted storytellers and listeners for many centuries. The emphasis in selecting contents for the book has been upon nonsense, ranging from intellectual humor and absurdity to a purely verbal nonsense based on the sounds and manipulations of words. Yet for all the nonsense, there is much wisdom and beauty of image, and in the rhythmical, often complex arrangements of words there is often a haunting poetry. Nearly every item in the book—whether song, chant or actual story—follows in its telling one or another of the narrative patterns which folklorists call "formula tales." I have added a few examples of other nonsense lore with high "formulaic" quality: a "punctuation rhyme," a handful of chain riddles, numskull stories, and little tall tales, and one full-fledged lying tale.

What are formula tales? Youngsters (and storytellers) love them dearly; because of all types of oral narrative they most resemble games. They have strict rules for telling, which may not be altered. Plot may have almost no importance. What delights the storyteller and the audience is a game-like patterning of words to some *verbally* logical conclusion; this can be ridiculous or sensible, but it must seem to emerge inevitably from a strict formalism in the telling. Folklore scholars have classified formula tales into chain stories (including cumulative tales), endless stories, and catch tales. Many narratives of each type are in the present book.

Catch tales are often mock tales rather than real stories, used by elders to tease children or to end a storytelling session: "Shall I tell you a tale of a frog?" "Yes!" "A frog has no tail." Or a story starting with exciting details can suddenly end "unfinished": "If you will wait till he has . . . lifted the lid, we will learn what wonderful things were in the box." (Grimm, No. 200, *The Golden Key*.) Scary stories ending with "Boo!" or any other tension-dissolving expression are catch tales. Teen-agers tell many catch stories, particularly mock ghost or horror stories with anticlimatic nonsense endings. In a favorite one the pursuit of much eerie "rap-rap-rapping" leads to a room full of "WRAPPING paper!" There are many other kinds of catch tales. Small children love catch dialogues, in which one tricks another into self-insult. One ends: ". . . 'There I saw a monkey,' 'Just like me.' " Another ends: ". . . 'I eight it.' 'Oh, you *ate* the old dead horse.' "

Endless stories, usually simple in form and very short, are of two main types. One kind leads quickly to a point where a single statement must be repeated endlessly: "Then another little ant (bee, locust) carried away another little grain of wheat (corn, oats), and then another little ant . . . ." or "Then another sheep (duck, etcetera) went across the stream." In India the story is often told of countless birds, who fly away one by one from a tree or snare. Sometimes a little story of this type is worked into a longer story, in which, for example, a king offers his daughter to the youth who can tell him a *very* long story; at last the king, bored by the interminable repetition, hushes the narrator and gives him the princess in marriage.

Another type of endless tale is the circular story or "round." Here the narrative device is for the story to lead back into its starting phrase and thus logically go on for ever. The circular story most frequently told in the United States goes: "It was a dark and stormy night. Some Indians were sitting round their campfire. One asked their chief to tell a story and he began, 'It was a dark and stormy night. . . .'" (The story is as often told of cowboys, robbers, or sailors.) A German children's song has more "plot": A dog came into the kitchen / And stole an egg from the cook. / The cook grabbed a ladle / And broke the dog in two. / A lot of dogs came / And dug him a grave, / And put a tombstone over it / On which was written: / *A dog came into the kitchen.* . . . American children know and chant many circular dialogues, for example: "That's tough!" "What's tough?" "Life." "What's life?" "A magazine." . . . "What does it cost?" "A quarter." "I've only got a dime." "That's tough!" etcetera. There are also circular "jokes" or "riddles": "Pete and Repeat were

sitting on a fence. Pete fell off. Who was left?" "Repeat."
"PETE AND REPEAT . . . ."

In the body of world folklore, most formula tales are
chain tales, which may be simple or cumulative. Chain
tales are so varied in form that they are easier to illustrate
than define, but in each some series—of numbers, words,
events, characters—is linked together in a formal relation-
ship that is maintained throughout the story. A very simple chain tale linking the days of the week is a nursery
rhyme: Solomon Grundy / Born on Monday / Chris-
tened on Tuesday / Married on Wednesday / Took ill on
Thursday / Worse on Friday / Died on Saturday / Buried
on Sunday. A classic chain story is based on numbers in
numerical progression: The inventor of chess asked a king
to pay him for his invention one grain of wheat for the
first square, two grains for the second square, four for the
third, eight for the fourth, and so on. At first this seemed
a small amount, but it proved greater than the king's
wealth.* Another curious chain story formula is a dia-
logue in which the "listener" always comments wrongly:
"Did your cabbage grow big . . .?" "Yes! as big as hats."
"That's good." "No, a goat . . . ate them up." "That's
bad." "No, I killed the goat and got a tubful of meat."
"That's good." "No, in smoking the sausage, I burnt
down . . . ." The airplane story "Good or Bad?" in this
volume is such a story in modern dress. In many chain
stories each new object, as introduced, becomes a new
link in the chain, as in children's link rhymes: I went to
the river, / Couldn't get across; / Jumped on a mule, /
Thought he was a horse; / Mule wouldn't pull, / Traded

* The same formula was once used in a popular "catch problem" in rural America. A
farmboy was asked, "If I hired you for a month, would you rather I paid you a dollar
a day, or a penny for the first day, two cents for the second, four cents for the third . . .?
When the boy said, "A dollar a day," he was told to get a pencil and figure out how
much money he had lost.

him for a bull; / Bull wouldn't holler, / Traded him for a dollar. . . . There are many chain rhymes, riddles, and songs (including game songs) in folklore. In a great chain folktale popular in India and other Eastern countries, Miss Mouse's parents, seeking the most powerful bridegroom in the world for her, go in turn to sun, cloud, wind, mountain (or wall, or statue of Buddha), and finally to a young mouse, whom she appropriately marries. Each has proved in some way to be more powerful than the previous one. Our related Cheremis story from Siberia shows the chain tale at its most elaborate development without the use of cumulative repetition.

Cumulative stories are chain stories in which the verbal game is at its greatest complexity. At each new episode all that has gone before must be repeated, and, as Stith Thompson says in *The Folktale,* "Most of the enjoyment, both in the listening and the telling . . . is in the successful manipulation of the ever-growing rigmarole." Like musical compositions with mounting crescendos of repeated motifs, such stories must be played through without error, and they often have great formal beauty. Many cumulative stories are of great antiquity. "The House That Jack Built," "The Old Woman and Her Pig," "The Mouse That Lost Its Tail," and "Henny-Penny" are very old ones, still known to almost every child in the English-speaking world. Formerly they were *told* to children, by grandparents, parents, and nurses. Now they are usually read aloud to them, at about the same age when they are learning the Mother Goose rhymes. They are so familiar, so much the property of the nursery, and so readily accessible in many books, that they are omitted from the present one. The reader will be reminded of them again and again by other stories, similar in construction and often with identical details, from many lands.

Nearly half the folklore in this book comes from the English-speaking world. The rest is from about thirty other countries or ethnic groups, though I have made little effort to represent nations or peoples as such. Instead, my aim has been to illustrate by amusing example how folktales, folksongs, rhymes, and chants travel freely from country to country and from language to language. Folklore runs round the world, often adding or dropping or altering a theme to fit the new cultural or linguistic environment. In a similar way the content of folklore moves between the categories of story, song, rhyme, and chant. Another aim has been to show that folklore, a very old human cultural trait, is still a very lively one. The oldest printed source from which I have taken a story is a book first printed in London in 1642; the story was already old then, and it is still frequently heard in rural America and elsewhere. Two or three little stories collected from teenagers in 1962 seem to be wholly "new"; yet they follow strictly the traditional structures of the types of formula stories to which they belong.*

C. W.

---

* A reader who wishes to know the full range and variety of formula stories in world folklore should consult Antti Aarne and Stith Thompson, *The Types of the Folktale* (1961), in which Types 2000–2340 are formula tales, briefly described, with many references to their sources. Similar information is in Stith Thompson's *Motif-Index of Folk Literature*, where Motifs Z0–Z99 cover the formula tales. The *Standard Dictionary of Folklore, Mythology and Legend* has good brief articles on formula tales, chain tales, cumulative stories, and cumulative songs. The fullest discussion and bibliography of formula lore is in Archer Taylor, "A Classification of Formula Tales," *The Journal of American Folklore*, 46 (1933:77–88), and in his much more complete treatment in German: "Formelmärchen," in *Handwörterbuch den Deutschen Märchen*, Lutz Mackensen, Ed., 2 vols., Berlin, 1934–40, Vol. 2, Pp. 164–91.

Notes and Comments

I have given full sources for all stories and other items. Most are printed here exactly as heard or originally presented, or are translated (by myself unless otherwise indicated) with careful adherence to the originals. A few stories are adapted, as slightly as possible, for clarity; a few others are retold simply. One story was constructed from a synopsis, and in three items considerable alterations of original content were made; the changes are fully described in the notes.

STRANGE STORY, p. 17, Charles Carroll Bombaugh, *Gleanings for the Curious from the Harvest Fields of Literature,* Philadelphia, 1874, 749–50. Punctuation rhyme. Commas would change nonsense to meaning. Its classic prototype, "I saw a peacock with a fiery tail," is in many Mother Goose books.

THE TRAVELS OF A FOX, p. 18, Clifton Johnson, *What They Say in New England and Other American Folklore* (Carl Withers, Ed.), Columbia University Press, New York, 1963, 191–94. First printed in *The Outlook,* 57 (1897: 689–91). Chain story from Massachusetts. Johnson was one of the first Americans to gather Anglo-American folklore intensively; his book contains much wonderful formula lore, including "The Old Woman and Her Pig," "The Little Mouse With the Long Tail," and "The Little Red Hen and the Wheat."

DRAT THE WIND, p. 22, Vance Randolph, *The Talking Turtle and Other Ozark Folktales,* Columbia University Press, New York, 1957, 61–62. Cumulative tale from Missouri or Oklahoma, adapted (by reducing dialect and euphemizing "profanity"). No one else has reported so extensively as Vance Randolph on the lore of an American region. His many books on Ozark folklore cover folk stories, music, language, beliefs, and customs.

THE GREEDY OLD FAT MAN, p. 24, Walter A. Barnes in *West Virginia Folklore,* 3 (1952: 2–3). Cumulative story. (This story and Good or Bad?, p. 32, were printed in Ben Botkin and Carl Withers, *The Illustrated Book of American Folklore,* Grosset and Dunlap, New York, 1958.)

THE JOHNNY CAKE, p. 27, Fanny D. Bergen, in *Journal of American Folklore,* 2 (1889: 60–62). Cumulative story from Ohio.

GOOD OR BAD? p. 32, Lee Martin, in *Hoosier Folklore Bulletin,* 7 (1948: 21). Chain tale (of contradictory extremes). Several variants were collected in 1962–63 by a friend from New York high-school boys.

THE WALK, p. 33, collected 1962 by a friend from a fifteen-year-old New York high-school boy. Cumulative story (which seems not to have been previously collected).

PETER WENT FISHING ON SUNDAY, p. 34, Mellinger E. Henry, *Songs Sung in the Southern Appalachians,* Mitre Press, London, n.d. [1933?], 221–22. "Scary" *cante fable.*

THE DARK AND STORMY NIGHT, p. 35, the most frequently heard circular story in the United States.

WHAT'S A SILLY QUESTION? p. 35 and THE SHAGGY DOG, p. 36, collected 1963 by a friend from two New York City high-school boys. Endless stories, the first one "circular."

AROUND THE CORNER, p. 37, frequently heard from teen-agers. Circular rhyme, sometimes used as an "insult rhyme." A close variant of this rhyme was published by Archer Taylor in 1940 in "Formelmärchen" (see full reference, p. 152, *fn.*), p. 191.

'TWAS MIDNIGHT, p. 37. "Backwards rhyme," known and chanted by children in all English-speaking countries.

STRANGE HOUSES, p. 38. Chain riddles, as remembered by editor from Missouri, c. 1910.

THE OLD LADY WHO SWALLOWED A FLY, p. 39, collected 1960, Washington, D.C. Cumulative nonsense song (often merely chanted), very popular and with many variants in contemporary childhood and teen-age tradition.

THE BEAR WENT OVER THE MOUNTAIN, p. 42, collected 1962 by Alta Jablow from a teen-age Brooklyn girl, who called it a "camp song." A nonsense chain song, it is unusually elaborate.

JEREMIAH, p. 44, contributed by Margaret Gillis Figh. Chain rhyme from Alabama.

JOHNNY MCGORRY AND THE RED STOCKING, p. 45, Charles Edward Brown, in *Hoosier Folklore Bulletin,* 2 (1943:20–21). "Unfinished" teasing story.

TINY TEASING TALES, p. 46, are sometimes used by adults to tease children and are often used by children as "jokes" or "riddles."

TEASING QUESTIONS, p. 47, have very ancient adult use in teasing children; the last two were a few decades ago sometimes used by rural literary societies as topics for mock debates.

A MILLION STORIES, p. 47, collected 1963 by Alta Jablow from a Brooklyn girl. A catch tale.

THE LOCUSTS AND THE OATS, p. 48, Gustave Lanctot, "Contes Populaires Canadiens," in *Journal of American Folklore,* 44 (1931: 225-94), 262. Canadian endless story, translated from French.

STORY OF A NICKEL AND A DIME, p. 49, Rafael Ramirez de Arellano, *Folklore Portorriqueño,* Madrid, 1926, 21-22. Cumulative chant (or song?) from Puerto Rico, translated from Spanish. (I have translated *mula* as "donkey."

THOUSANDS AND THOUSANDS OF DUCKS, p. 52, *ibid,* 20. Endless story from Puerto Rico, translated from Spanish.

THE HERON'S BALL, p. 53, from a large body of unpublished folktales collected 1947-50 by Carl Withers in Mayajigua, Las Villas, Cuba. Cumulative story, translated from Spanish.

THE ELEPHANTS, p. 55, Florestan Fernandes, *Folclore e Mudança Social na Cidade de São Paulo,* São Paulo, Brazil, 1961, 63. Endless teasing chant, translated from Portuguese. (The author gives several such chants which, he says, children and adolescents use to annoy peers or adults considered boring or who can't take a joke. Fernandes' book is the most intensive study yet made by any anthropologist or other social scientist of the content and uses of children's folklore.)

THE PRETTY BIRD, p. 56, Ramon A. Laval, in "Cuentos de Nunca Acabar," *Revista de Folklore Chileno,* 1 (1910), 13-14. Endless story from Chile, translated from Spanish.

TEENY-TINY, p. 59, James Orchard Halliwell, *Popular Rhymes and Nursery Tales* (first edition), London, 1849, 25-26. Scary formula tale from England. (The "formula" is mainly in the reiteration of the words "teeny-tiny.")

TITTY MOUSE AND TATTY MOUSE, p. 62, James Orchard Halliwell, *The Nursery Rhymes of England* (fifth edition), London and New York, 1886, 295-98. Cumulative story. I have modernized "besom" to "broom" and "form" to "bench."

IN A DARK WOOD, p. 67, Iona and Peter Opie, *The Lore and Language of School Children,* Oxford University Press, London and New

York, 1959, 36. A "scary" chain chant, from England. (Strangely, much effort has failed to find this enchanting item in the current tradition of American children. The book from which it is taken is both a literary delight and a masterly presentation of the contemporary folklore of British children.)

MEET-ON-THE-ROAD, p. 68, Pamela Glenconner (later Lady Grey), *The White Wallet,* London, 1912, 348. This chain rhyme or song is called "An Ancient Piece of Folk-Lore" and is presumably from England. It is related to Child ballad no. 3, of which one variant begins: "O whare are ye gaun?"/Quo the fause knicht upon the road./"I'm gaun to the scule,"/Quo the boy, and still he stude.

THE KEY OF THE KINGDOM, p. 70, James Orchard Halliwell, *The Nursery Rhymes of England,* London, 1842, 115. A chain chant.

THE BIG CABBAGE AND THE BIG KETTLE, p. 71, James Howell, *Instructions for Forreine Travell,* London, 1869 (first published, London, 1642), 64, retold in modern English. This tall tale of rival story tellers, from an English source over three hundred years old, is still a favorite among tall tale tellers.

THE TAIL, p. 71, John Francis Campbell, *Popular Tales of the West Highlands* (new series, 4 vols.), Paisley and London, 1890–93, v. 2, 494. An "unfinished" catch tale from Scotland, translated from Gaelic by Campbell.

THE CAT'S TAIL, p. 72, F. Adolpho Coelho, *Contos Populares Portuguezes,* Lisbon, 1878, 19–20. Chain tale (of trick exchanges) from Portugal, translated from Portuguese.

IN PARIS THERE IS A STREET, p. 75, Eugene Rolland, *Rimes et Jeux de l'Enfance,* Paris, 1883, 125. French chain chant, translated from French.

THE BIG, BIG, RABBIT, p. 76, Jean-François Bladé, *Contes Populaires de la Gascogne* (3 vols.), Paris, 1886, v. 3, p. 267–71. Chain nonsense story from France, translated from French.

THE THREE HUNTERS, p. 77, *do,* 254–55. Nonsense tall tale (of "logical impossibilities"), translated from French.

WHEN THE BULL BELLOWS, p. 78, from *Melusine,* 1 (1878), col. 264. Chain riddle, translated from French.

MR. LOUSE AND MRS. LOUSE, p. 79, written from the summary of a Belgian (Walloon) story given in G. Laporte, "Les Contes

Wallons," Folklore Fellows Communications, No. 101, Helsinki, 1932, 138. Cumulative story.

THE DAY THE SKY FELL, p. 81, ("Die Dumme Tierlein"), Paul Zaunert, *Deutsche Märchen seit Grimm,* Jena, 1922, 285-86. German cumulative story, translated from German.

A MEETING OF TWO SERVANTS, p. 85, Grimms' *Household Tales* (many editions in English since 1884), No. 140. German sing-song chain tale.

THE BOY WHO OUTFIBBED A PRINCESS, p. 86, Sir G. W. Dasent, "That's a Story," *Popular Tales from the Norse,* (second edition), London and New York, *n.d.,* 122-23. A Norwegian "lying tale," retold. (The brother's first lie here is invented to replace the original one: a gravid cow drops her calf before she can walk across the field.)

THE BOY AND THE FOX, p. 89, G. Djurklo, *Fairy Tales from the Swedish.* F. A. Stokes, New York, 1901, 85-86. Numskull story (of air-castles), slightly adapted.

THE FIREFLY, p. 90, Giovanni Giannini, *Scioglilingua, Indovinelli, Giuochi, Fanciulleschi, Canzonette, Filastrocche, e Storielle Popolari,* Florence, Italy, 1907, 46-48. Chain story from Italy, translated from Italian.

A LONG ONE AND A SHORT ONE, p. 92, Thomas Frederick Crane, *Italian Popular Tales,* Boston and New York, 1885, 371. Italian catch (teasing) tale.

THE COCK AND THE HEN, p. 95, A. N. Afanasyev, *Russian Folktales* (title in Russian), 3 vols., Moscow, 1957, v. 1, 98. Chain story, translated from Russian by Dr. Sula Benet, New York City.

THE VISIT, p. 97, *ibid,* v. 3, 446. Chain chant, translated from Russian by Dr. Sula Benet. (The lines "Where is the water?"/"It ran into the mountain." are inserted, from Dr. Benet's childhood memory, to fill a hiatus in the printed story.)

THE TURNIP, p. 98, as told by Dr. Sula Benet, 1964, from childhood memory. Cumulative nonsense story.

WHO IS STRONGEST? p. 100, Arvid Genetz, "Ost-Tscheremississche Sprachstudien," in *La Journal Finno-Ougrienne,* Helsinki, 7 (1889: 1-185), 82. Chain story from the Cheremis people of Siberia, translated from German.

THE LITTLE BIRD THAT FOUND THE PEA, p. 102, *The Calcutta Review,*

Vol. 51, 116-18. Cumulative story from India, slightly adapted. (It is called a "Hindu child's story.")

THE LOUSE AND THE CROW, p. 108, E. M. Gordon, *Indian Folk Tales and Proverbs*, London, 1908, 60-63. Cumulative tall tale from India, slightly adapted.

THE STORY OF IR, BIR, DAU, AND I, p. 112, E. M. Gordon, *Indian Folk-Tales, Being Sidelights on Village Life in Bitaspore, Central Provinces*, London, 1909, 69-72, adapted. Indian nonsense chain song. (Gordon collected the song from a young girl who sang it to attract a crowd for a beggar whom she accompanied.)

THE ANT AND THE FROG, p. 115, Edward Stack and Charles Lyall, *The Mikirs*, London, 1908, 46-48. A chain story, slightly adapted, of the Mikir, a hill tribe of Central Assam.

THE BEGGAR AND THE RICE, p. 119, Katherine Neville Fleeson, *Laos Folklore of Farther India*, New York, 1889, 83. Numskull story (of air castles), slightly adapted.

THE TALE OF A FROG, p. 120, A. Landes, *Contes Tjames*, Saigon, 1887, 115-16. A children's chain song from the Shan people of Southern Annam, translated from French. I have euphemized the French word "derrière" to "back" and described the herdboy's stomach as "empty" instead of "swollen" (from hunger).

WHO IS MIGHTIEST? p. 122, Hans Nevermann, *Die Rieskugel: Sagen und Göttergeschichten, Märchen, Fabeln und Schwänke aus Vietnam*, Eisenach, 1952, 135. A dilemma chain tale from Vietnam, translated from German.

PLOP! p. 123, *Folk Tales from China* (Second Series), Foreign Languages Press, Peking, 1958, 30-32. Cumulative tale from Tibet. This is an odd version of "Henny Penny" and "The Day the Sky Fell," since the cumulative technique has been almost wholly abandoned in the telling.

A PRINCE WENT HUNTING, p. 126, C. Arendt, "On Chinese Apologues," in *China Review*, 13 (1884-85: 23-24), 23-24. This chain-of-circumstances story was extracted by Arendt from an early Chinese novel. I have changed the telling from first person to third and slightly modernized the English.

CHINESE RIVAL STORYTELLERS, p. 128, Herbert A. Giles, *Quips from a Chinese Jest-Book*, Shanghai, 1925, 143-44. Chinese tall tale, retold.

THE RATS OF NAGASAKI, p. 129, Keigo Seki (Editor), *Folktales of Japan,* translated by Robert J. Adams. University of Chicago Press, Chicago, 1963, 30. Japanese endless story.

THE FROGS OF YONDER MOUNTAIN CRY, p. 130, Lafcadio Hearn, *Japanese Miscellany.* Little, Brown and Co., Boston, 1901 (reprinted 1954 by Charles E. Tuttle, Rutland, Vermont, and Tokyo), 173. Japanese endless children's song, slightly adapted.

THE TYRANNICAL KING, p. 131, Dean Fansler, *Filipino Popular Tales,* American Folklore Society, Memoir 12 (1921), 388-89. Chain tale from the Philippine Islands, slightly adapted.

HOW A BOY GOT A BABOON, p. 135, Rev. C. F. Schlenker, *A Collection of Temne Traditions,* London, 1861, 57-61. Cumulative story from the Temne people of Sierra Leone or Liberia, West Africa. Slightly adapted for clarity.

HOW A YOUNG MAN BECAME A CHIEF, p. 140, Blaise Cendrars, *The African Saga,* Payson & Clarke, Ltd., New York, 1927, 260-62. Chain story from the Sukumu (Waissu Kuma) people of Tanganyika. Adapted for clarity.

THE BIG TREE AND THE BIG BIRD, p. 142, ("Rival Storytellers"), Alta Jablow, *Yes and No: The Intimate Folklore of Africa,* Horizon Press, New York, 1961, 208-09. A tall tale from the Vai people of Liberia.

THE HUNTERS AND THE ANTELOPE, p. 143, and WHO WAS MOST SKILLFUL? p. 143, Leo Frobenius and Douglas C. Fox, "Improbable Tales", *African Genesis,* Stackpole Sons, New York, 1937, 153-55. African tall tales (mock dilemma stories) from the Mandingo (Mande) people of the Western Sudan. The first is slightly adapted.

GOSO THE TEACHER, p. 144, Edward Steere, *Swahili Tales,* London, 1889, 285-91. Cumulative story from Zanzibar, slightly adapted.

About the Author

CARL WITHERS, anthropologist and folklorist, is the author of the much loved A ROCKET IN MY POCKET: *The Rhymes and Chants of Young Americans,* as well as several other important folklore anthologies for young people.

Born and raised on a Missouri farm, Mr. Withers attended Harvard College. For several years after graduation he taught English, and he has worked in the publishing field. But his interests turned to anthropology, which he studied at Columbia University. He is well-known in this field for a book called *Plainville, U.S.A.,* which he published under the pseudonym James West.

Mr. Withers has spent over 25 years at research, at writing, and at compiling or anthologizing folklore material from all over the world. For years he has been collecting from children and teen-agers their own folklore: their rhymes and chants, jokes and riddles, sayings and superstitions, stories, songs, and games. His work, in anthropology and folklore, has taken him to countries of Europe, the Caribbean, and South America. I SAW A ROCKET WALK A MILE, the first compilation for young readers of worldwide "formula" folk stories, chants and songs, represents intensive fieldwork and library study.

Now a resident of New York City, Mr. Withers is presently working on an anthropological book based on his field research experiences in Cuba, as well as on a study of the content and function of folklore in the life of a small American farming community.